FOSSIL AMPHI
AND REPTI

PLATE I

DIMORPHODON

Frontispiece

FOSSIL AMPHIBIANS
AND REPTILES

by

W. E. SWINTON

FIFTH EDITION

First Edition	.	.	*1954*
Second Edition	.	.	*1958*
Third Edition	.	.	*1962*
Fourth Edition	.	.	*1965*
Fifth Edition	.	.	*1973*

Publication No. 543

ISBN 0 565 00543 X

 Printed in England by Staples Printers Limited
at their Kettering, Northants, establishment

PREFACE

If the galleries of a modern museum of natural history are arranged to give a comprehensive survey of the products of nature as observed and classified by man, and to suggest the conclusions which man has reached concerning their history and relationships, then a museum handbook will be of most value if it condenses this evidence into a connected whole on the printed page rather than by providing a topographical guide to cases and their contents. Dr. W. E. Swinton's new handbook on *Fossil Amphibians and Reptiles* aims at giving a conspectus of the subject which can not only be used by the visitor in the galleries but perused at leisure subsequently. It includes, moreover, sufficient detail to be of value to the advanced student as well as the general reader. Based on the rich series of fossils in the Department of Geology, it refers where necessary to material in other museums, and also draws attention to important gaps in the national collection.

Asterisks after the names of fossils in the text indicate that specimens are on exhibition; genera not so marked may of course be represented in the reserve collections.

The handbook is embellished with ten new reconstructions of fossil amphibians and reptiles by Maurice Wilson, and the cover design is by Anthony Whishaw. There are forty-eight new line drawings by D. E. Woodall, and most of the remaining illustrations are taken from the former *Guide to the Fossil Birds, Reptiles and Amphibians*, now out of print and superseded. The birds will be dealt with at a later date in a separate handbook.

April 1954

W. N. EDWARDS,
Keeper of Geology

PREFACE TO FIFTH EDITION

The text of this further edition of Professor W. E. Swinton's handbook is largely unchanged, but it incorporates a number of emendations and additions necessitated by recent research. In addition a new geological time-scale is appended.

H. W. BALL,

November 1971   Keeper of Palaeontology

CONTENTS

LIST OF PLATES

I. INTRODUCTION

The study of fossil amphibians and reptiles is not just an obscure piece of research only of academic interest, it is a necessary part of the understanding of the history of living things.

From the early and primitive forms of life, in the course of the ages, a large and diversified company of animals was developed; at first without any hard parts in or around their bodies but later, in many cases, bearing shells of lime or of horn. Life was millions of years old before the first animals with bone in their structure were evolved, the primitive ostracoderms that came on the scene in Ordovician and Silurian times (see *Geological Chart*, p. 124).

From that distant day to this the backboned creatures have spread into every element. Ostracoderms gave way to fishes and fishes to amphibians, which first took steps to establish themselves on the land. One kind of these amphibians gave origin to the reptiles which for many millions of years were the principal animals on land, in the sea and in the air. The present handbook is a brief account of these interrelated amphibians and reptiles. This, however, is only a part of a long and involved story. From the reptiles in the Triassic there were derived presumably the birds and almost certainly the mammals, and from these and the remnants of the other groups, there has descended the rich, varied, and largely familiar fauna of the world today. Accompanying the evolution of animal life there was a comparable progress in the plant kingdom: from the original minute specks of life to the seaweeds, through the first land plants, on to the varied vegetation that we can now see.

From this preliminary statement several important points emerge. Firstly, that life has not always been of the same kind; secondly, that our evidence shows it has increased in complexity in the course of time much as many individual animals or plants increase in complexity during their own life history; thirdly, that in the study of life's history (or Palaeontology) we have always to consider the question of time.

How do we discover the evolutionary stages of plants and animals which lived in the past? And how do we date them? These questions are best answered by a consideration of the fate of an animal on its death.

If the animal dies in the sea its body may slowly sink to the bottom of the water, there to embed itself in the sand or mud. If the animal, like a jelly-fish, has no hard parts, it may completely disintegrate and disappear. If it has, however, a shell or skeleton of lime or bone, then this hard substance may remain, becoming in course of time overlain by an ever-increasing thickness of material. After a very considerable time this mud or sand may become hardened into a rock. Studies in Geology (the science of the earth) show us that rocks are seldom left undisturbed. The rock mass may become high and dry through the retreat of the waters, or the rock series may be thrown up into folds by the movement of a whole region of the earth's surface. There are countless examples of such happenings all over the world, and many can be seen very well in Britain.

The specimen entombed in the rocks may be destroyed by such movements and the pressures involved. On the other hand, the elevation or tilting of the layer in which the specimen lies, brings the rock under the influence of wind and rain, frost and snow, the heat of the sun by day and the comparative coolness of the air at night. Disintegration or erosion of the rocks is brought about by such forces, by rivers slowly cutting their way through the land, and in coastal regions by the waves of the sea. In breaking up the rocks naturally by these means, or artificially through engineering works undertaken by men, the specimen may once again be disclosed. It may, of course, be greatly altered by pressure, or by chemical change brought about by the infiltration of solutions during its entombment, but it will have been "dug out" naturally or mechanically and so is called a fossil (Latin—*fossilis*—dug out or dug up).

Much the same sequence will be involved if the animal died on land and if its remains were subsequently removed by streams, though here the chances of preservation of a complete animal or skeleton are much less likely. Where an animal dies on land and its remains are not removed by some agency, or are not covered up by sand or other deposit, disintegration will inevitably take place and nothing at all may remain. Fossils may therefore give a nearly complete picture of an individual or a small community, but not all forms of life are equally represented in the geological record.

In the last two or three hundred years very many fossils have been collected and, especially within the last hundred years, intensive research has been done upon them. Normally only hard parts of an animal are well represented in fossils, but traces of soft parts are occasionally found. Among fossil amphibians and reptiles, for example, traces of the outlines of the original body have been seen, the pattern of the skin has been preserved in several instances, and fossilized eggs have been discovered. From the study of all the evidence we have a fairly extensive knowledge of life in the past,

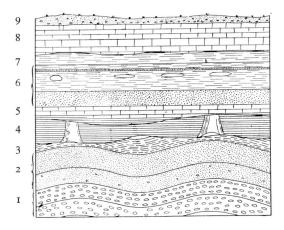

Fig. 1.—Rocks as records of geological history.

In this imaginary section of the earth's crust the sequence of events is indicated by the rocks as: conglomerates (1) show that the region was under the sea and was gradually subsiding, with the formation of sand and standstone (2) until there was comparatively deep water in which mud accumulated to form the clay (3).

Earth movements then resulted in the folding, uplifting and partial wearing away of the strata formed and dry land conditions prevailed for a time, as can be seen from the fossil tree stumps (4). Slow subsidence led to the formation of a fresh-water lake with deposits of clay, limestone and fresh-water fossils (5), until once again elevation and a change in climate resulted in desert conditions as revealed by red sandstones and marls with salt and gypsum deposits (6).

A further subsidence of the land led to the gradual return of the sea, at first shallow and muddy so that brackish deposits (7) were formed, but later becoming deep and clear, with the formation of limestone, containing marine fossils (8). Finally the land was again raised, the sea retreated, and dry land conditions, with the formation of soil (9), prevail.

(Modified from North, *Coal, and the Coalfields in Wales*, by permission.)

both plant and animal. The rocks in which the fossils are preserved often reveal clues as to the topographical and climatic conditions in which they were laid down, thus presenting a more or less satisfactory idea of the background of the once living creatures.

The study of fossils also tells us about the similarities between different animals. In many cases animals look alike because they live in the same kind of way. Thus the modern sharks and the whales and dolphins are superficially alike, though the sharks are cold-blooded fishes and the others are warm-blooded mammals. The fishes have always been swimming animals, whereas the whales are descendants of land animals and have only secondarily become adapted for life in water. Such superficial resemblance is known as convergence.

Then again we can determine from the fossil evidence whole groups of animals that are related to each other and in the scale of time can trace lines of ancestry and descent leading to and from these groups. We can thus discover much of the route along which evolution has worked.

The actual relationships of the layers of rock in which fossils are found are obviously important in this study. These layers (beds or strata), although they may appear to be of limited distribution locally, can often actually be traced, through borings, cuttings, or stream and river banks for many hundreds of miles. The rocks that were laid down in water, or less often on dry land, the so-called sedimentary rocks, were deposited one upon another (see Fig. 1). Where they have remained comparatively undisturbed the sequence of the rocks is itself an indication of succession in time. The younger rocks are above and progressively older rocks are underneath. In other places, though the original order of these rocks has been altered by folding and cracking (faulting), geologists can usually disentangle the succession. The time that deposition of sediments takes can be observed in many places today. The maximum thickness of most of the geological layers or beds is known and the time that such layers originally took to form can therefore be estimated. Such calculations are, of course, only approximations, and it is fortunate for us that much more accurate methods employing physico-chemical observations on the disintegration of radio-active substances in the rocks have been developed. A large number of observations of this kind have been made all over the world so that the ages of rocks of sedimentary origin and of volcanic origin can be dated in years. The *Geological Chart* gives the result of some of the data obtained from all these sources.

The Palaeontological Department of the Museum contains more than a million specimens of fossils, though the amphibians and reptiles number only about twenty thousand. These great collections are among the foremost in the world, but there are many others and taken together they constitute a vast reservoir of knowledge from which the following account of the early vertebrates is derived.

4

II. THE STUDY OF VERTEBRATES

The amateur need not be disconcerted by the apparent complexities of the anatomy and physiology of vertebrates. The information which will be necessary for his understanding of the following pages can be derived fairly simply from a knowledge of his own structure and processes. This is largely because the anatomists of old transferred most of the terms of human anatomy and physiology to the animals they studied. Thus most of the bones, even in the reptiles and amphibians, bear the same names as those of their human counterparts. There are, of course, profound differences in the method of birth, respiration, heat regulation and feeding between these kinds of animals and ourselves.

Most amphibians and reptiles lay eggs; for the former, moist surroundings are needed; that is to say, something of the original environment is required for the egg and it is consequently laid, often in considerable numbers, in water. The egg of a reptile, on the other hand, is laid on dry or nearly dry soil, the necessary fluid being contained within the non-porous shell. A few amphibians and reptiles retain the egg within the body of the mother until it hatches so that the young are produced as free-living animals. The egg-laying condition is known as oviparous; that in which the eggs are retained for hatching is known as ovo-viviparous.

Young amphibians breathe by gills during their early stages, but in most forms the gills are lost later and the adult breathes by lungs. The reptile never has gills and throughout the course of its life is an air-breather, though not in exactly the same way as are the mammals. The mammal, for example—as we know from our own experience—can breathe and eat at the same time usually without any obstruction of the passages, but in most of the lower vertebrates this is not the case and breathing and eating are done alternately by gulping movements; generally the amphibian and reptilian nose and throat passages are simpler than those of the mammals, but one or two reptilian exceptions to this are dealt with in later pages.

It is important to remember that the life of these lower animals is lived at a slower tempo than that of mammals. Amphibians and reptiles are cold-blooded, which means that they, unlike the mammals, have no constant body temperature but are affected by their

5

environment to a considerable extent. The reptiles, for example, are heated by the sun and cooled by the chill at night, but they are also heated by physical exercise and this heat is generated in accordance with the cube of the animal's weight, whereas it is radiated and lost according to the square of the surface. There may thus be a preponderance of heat generated on activity which is lost slowly during the long rests after bursts of movement.

Amphibians, reptiles, birds and mammals are all classed together as tetrapods or four-limbed animals. In their essential structure these limbs are much like our own. In the fore limb there is an upper bone or humerus between the shoulder and the elbow. Below the elbow there are the two characteristic bones, the radius and the ulna, terminating at the wrist. The wrist or carpus is a complex of small bones allowing a wide range of movement and supporting in most cases the five digits or fingers. This five-fingered condition is primitive and common throughout the tetrapods, but several of the fingers may be lost in the evolution of some groups, and there is much variation in the proportion of the bones and particularly in the length of the digits. Examples of these will be dealt with from time to time.

The fore limbs are attached to the body by means of muscles which are themselves largely bound to a series of bones at the side and in the breast which are together known as the shoulder girdle. The shoulder girdle consists usually of the coracoid, scapula, clavicle (collar-bone) and interclavicle, though the clavicle and interclavicle may be reduced or lost in some forms, and there may be an additional element, the cleithrum, in others. (See fig. 4).

The hind limb also has a series of bones comparable with our own. There is a single upper bone, the femur, joining the hip girdle and knee. In the knee itself the patella or knee-cap is wanting in amphibians and reptiles, but below the knee joint there are the two characteristic bones, the tibia or shin-bone and the fibula. The ankle or tarsus is a complex of small bones much like the carpus and giving support and articulation to the five toes of the foot. There are differences in the proportionate lengths of these bones and there are modifications in accordance with the pose or method of walking. Nearly all amphibians and most reptiles used all four limbs in progression, but many important reptiles were bipedal. Once again there may be great lengthening of the toes. In the reptiles that were adapted for swimming and in the land reptile there was frequently a reduction in their number, the first and fifth digits often being reduced or lost.

The hip girdle consists essentially of three bones: an upper bone or ilium, an anterior and downwardly pointing pubis and a posterior and downwardly pointing ischium on each side. These two latter sets of bones are often united to one another below; the ilia above, attached in one way or another to the vertebral column, provide a fixed support for the attachment of the muscles of the hind limb and for the top of the femur.

The vertebral column consists of a long and numerous series of bobbin-like pieces of bone, or centra. In some forms the vertebrae are all much alike; in others they are clearly differentiated into regions such as the neck or cervical series, the body or dorsal series, the sacral series with one or more attachments to the hip girdle, and the vertebrae of the tail or caudal series. Immediately above this line of centra throughout most of its length, and protected by the upper, or neural, processes of the vertebrae, lies the important nerve cord (the spinal cord) which in front is continuous directly with the brain.

The skull of amphibians and reptiles varies greatly in size, in the amount of bone that is developed and in the relative proportions of the facial and the cranial (or hinder) portions. Some of the skulls have very long snouts. All of these skulls have essentially two pairs of openings: the nostrils, the comparatively small openings for the intake of air, and the orbits or eye apertures. In many amphibians the external opening of the ear is a notch or bay at the back of the skull, and only in some of the latest forms is this opening surrounded by bone. In many reptiles there is no specific opening in the skull, as in mammals, for an external auditory meatus. In both amphibians and reptiles the mechanics of hearing are somewhat simpler than in the mammal, for a single bone, the stapes, connects the tympanum or ear-drum at the surface with the oval window of the inner ear. Vibrations are therefore directly transmitted from the ear-drum to the receptive apparatus within the skull.

The hinder part of the skull on its upper surface or its sides sometimes shows openings, which are really arches of bones that serve for the attachment of muscles for the movement of the lower jaw or the movement of the skull upon the neck and shoulders.

In the reptiles one of the bases of classification is the position and number of these openings or temporal fossae. Skulls without such

7

B

openings are said to be anapsid (without arches), others are known as parapsid, or synapsid, according to whether the single opening is on the upper part or the side of the skull, or diapsid where both upper and lower openings occur on each half of the skull (Fig. 14).

In many of the amphibians and reptiles there is also a single opening behind the orbits known as the pineal foramen. This small aperture marks the position of the once functional pineal or third eye. In some early forms it no doubt served a visual function, but in later forms this was lost and the opening became very small or even closed. A vestigial third eye exists in the living *Sphenodon*.

The jaws in these groups can often open widely and their connexion with the upper jaw is frequently far back in the skull. The connexions are quite different from those of the mammals and man.

The teeth also vary greatly in number and in position. Teeth are borne on the jaws themselves or on the palate, but are sometimes absent from the back of the jaws, or sometimes from the front. In a few forms which will be discussed later no teeth at all are developed, though this condition is rare. Reptilian teeth may be attached to the rim of the jaws or inserted in sockets, but in nearly all cases the succession and replacement of teeth was continuous—a condition which is known as polyphyodont.

In the pages that follow the details of the structure and evolution of the various groups are given. Structure is of great importance for two reasons. Firstly, because the appearance of animals may belie the structure within and thus animals of entirely different history and relationship, such as the ichthyosaur and shark may come to look much alike due to their adaptation for a similar kind of life. Secondly, the structure of animals is important because it gives the clue to lines of evolution and to true relationship; it therefore forms the basis of classification.

The study of amphibians and reptiles can produce results of interest in a number of different ways. It may disclose a great deal of the life history, the development and the habitat of the individual animal. It can help to unravel the tangled skein of evolution in groups that have been long dead and were never seen alive by man. It helps to explain the anatomical and physiological bases upon which all living animals inevitably depend.

*   *   *   *

For convenience, fossil animals, like living animals, must have names, though these are frequently of little value in the understanding of the animal. What is known as the binominal classification is used throughout. This indicates the genus and species: the species is the whole name, as in *Crocodylus niloticus*, the Nile Crocodile; the genus is the first of these names, *Crocodylus*. In palaeontology the characters that indicate specific or generic relationship or alleged relationship vary from group to group and are sometimes matters of dispute. Among living animals one criterion of a species is that members of it should be able to breed fertile offspring, but with fossils it is obviously not possible to use such a criterion.

Next in rank above the genus is the family, which is usually indicated by the ending "idae", as in Crocodylidae. Above the family is the Order, as Crocodilia. Whereas the specific name *Crocodylus niloticus* gives some clue to the range or occurrence of the animal, scientific names are often derived from the name of the discoverer or from some comparatively trivial characteristic of the specimen. For example, *Diplodocus*, one of the largest and most frequently figured dinosaurs, means "double beam", a reference to two little bones that occur below the tail vertebrae and may be likened to skids.

In scientific literature the generic and specific names are usually printed in italics, followed often by the author's name which should be in Roman type. When the author's name is in brackets, this indicates that the species described by the original author has since been transferred to another genus.

III. THE ORIGIN OF THE AMPHIBIA

The derivation of four-legged animals (tetrapods) from fish ancestors raises several problems. The transition must have been accomplished gradually and the first amphibian must therefore have had very close similarity with members of the parent fish group. Though we have not found all the transitional stages, the so-called missing links, of this story, we can determine fairly well the course that the evolution must have taken.

The requirements of the new mode of life, which was nothing less than the first invasion of the land by backboned animals, were twofold. First, there must have been complete adaptability of the limbs for the new kind of movement in the new medium; fins had to become legs. Of all the fishes that we know there was only one group that gave promise or foreshadowed the possibility of such an adaptation. Secondly, there must have been ability to breathe air regularly. Oddly enough this appears to have been less difficult, for two related groups of fishes were able to do so.

These two kinds of fish were the Dipnoans or "lung-fish" and the extinct Rhipidistia, and of the two the Rhipidistia were those that could also have developed the land limbs. Further, they have characters in the skull and in their teeth that are common to the amphibia.

The answer to the question as to why the amphibia should have been developed must be found in the geographical conditions of the period. The time was during the late Devonian when we have evidence of prolonged dry spells during which the fresh-water pools were subject to great reduction in depth and exten... when consequently many fishes died out. Obviously an... ...ould accommodate itself to these conditions was in a ... ntageous position. The Dipno... ...r scattered but degenerate remnan... ...uth America, South Africa and Australia. ...Rh... did so too. It must, however, have been a very great a... advantage if the stranded fish could not only breathe but eat. The Rhipidistians were carnivores, living upon other fishes, and in the drying pools and even on the dry shores there would be considerable numbers of fish alive or moribund to supply them for a time. If, however,

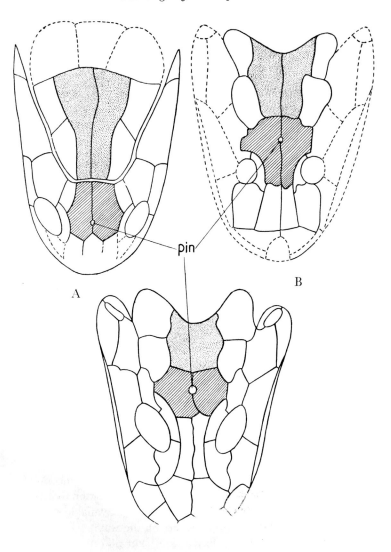

Fig. 2.—The fish-amphibia transition. Skulls of A, *Osteolepis*, a fish; B, *Elpistostege* C, *Ichthyostega*. The upper surface shows the gradual pulling back of the orbits, postorbital region, and the relative position of the pineal foramen. The parietals, enclosing the pineal foramen, are shaded diagonally, the postparietal bones are stippled; pin, pineal foramen. [After Westoll.]

one form was able to crawl over the flats of mud and sand in search of food and still extant pools, then the survival value of this ability was enormous. The conquest of the land must have been accidental, for as yet there was little there for large carnivores to eat. But for long they must have lived as "four-footed fishes".

From discoveries that have been made in Scotland, from Escuminac Bay, on the Gaspé Peninsula, Canada, and especially from

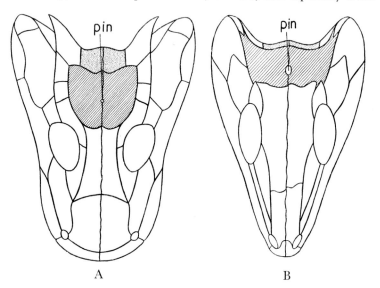

Fig. 3.—An amphibian skull, A, *Palaeogyrinus* and a reptile (Cotylosaur) skull; B, *Romeria* showing a continuation of the process of reduction and retraction of the parietal bones and the position of the pineal foramen; pin, pineal foramen.
[After Westoll.]

Greenland, we have a series of finds, often tantalizingly incomplete, that show the way in which the fish-amphibian transition took place. As we have said, the break is not bridged by the available evidence, but these specimens are stepping-stones on the way.

We have from Escuminac Bay a skull (but no other part of the skeleton) of a form called *Elpistostege*, intermediate between fishes and amphibians, and from beds in Greenland, that may be late Devonian, there are animals that have been called *Ichthyostega** and *Ichthyostegopsis*. The last are of predominantly amphibian type, but they still bear a few traces of fish ancestry including the possession of a tail supported by fin-rays. The skulls of the group (now

PLATE 2

AN ICHTHYOSTEGALIAN

called the Ichthyostegalia) link up with similar skulls of definitely Carboniferous age (*Palaeogyrinus; Eogyrinus*) of which there are some skeletal remnants, and these are quite similar to the same regions of well-known fossil amphibians (Plate 2). The story is not so easy as all this and there are controversies about it. It is unfortunate that little of this early amphibian material is available in this Museum, but the significant changes that took place may be indicated in the figures showing comparison with skulls and other regions of the fishes and the amphibians (Figs 2, 3, 4).

Even in early Carboniferous times it is clear that there were several lines of development among amphibians. These will be indicated and the main characters described and figured in the next chapter.

IV. FOSSIL AMPHIBIA

The principal changes in the skull and the skeleton of the amphibians as contrasted with those of their fish ancestors are due to the mechanical demands of life without the constant support of the buoyancy of water. There is no doubt that for long the two groups were closely associated in habitats and habits, that they lived more or less side by side. In the varied circumstances mentioned earlier, during a sufficiency of water the fishes were the better off; in times of drought the amphibians had advantages.

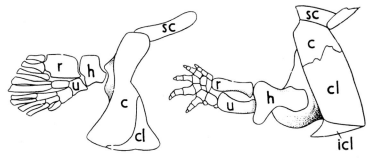

Fig. 4.—The fish-amphibian transition. The shoulder girdle of the Devonian Rhipidistian fish *Sauripterus* (left) compared with the diagram of the primitive tetrapod (right). [After Romer.]
sc, supracleithrum; c, cleithrum; cl, clavicle; icl, interclavicle; h, humerus; r, radius; u, ulna.

The diagrams (Figs 2, 3, 4) show the results of the adjustments that were made in the skull and limb bones and in their supports.

Primitive amphibians share with the Rhipidistian fishes the possession of a plate-like skull, though, as can be seen from the figures, the bones have different proportions. The teeth too are closely similar. In contrast, however, the true amphibians have the back of the skull relatively free from the shoulder girdle and have no operculum or gill-cover. The skull of the earliest amphibians articulates with the backbone by means of a single condyle, a rounded ball-like process that fits into a cup formed by the portions of the first vertebra of the neck, though in the later forms, and in all those now living, there is a double articular condyle.

Traces of the canals for the lateral-line sensory organs persist on the skulls of many fossil amphibians.

There are, of course, differences in the jaws. The upper jaw of amphibians is firmly fixed to the skull and one of the bones used in the support of the fish jaw—the hyomandibular—becomes of great importance as part of the hearing apparatus. The lower jaw moves on a kind of rocker at the back of the skull, thus allowing a wide opening of the mouth.

The disappearance of the operculum mentioned above has led to the spiracle of fishes becoming the otic notch of the primitive

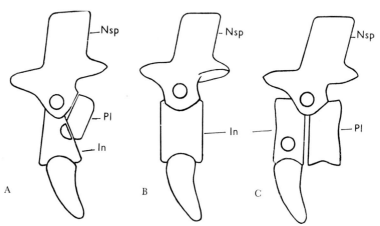

Fig. 5.—A, Rhachitomous vertebra. Neural spine resting on intercentrum and small pleurocentrum; B, Stereospondylous vertebra. Neural spine resting on intercentrum; C, Embolomerous vertebra. Neural spine resting on pleurocentrum and intercentrum. Nsp, neural spine; In, intercentrum; Pl, pleurocentrum. Half natural size.

amphibian. This opening becomes closed by the tympanum, or ear-drum, and the fish hyomandibular already mentioned becomes the rod-like stapes connecting the tympanum with the inner ear and so transmitting by shock even the comparatively gentle vibrations of the air.

The upper and lower jaws are toothed, as in the fishes, and remnants of the series of teeth upon the palate still remain.

The loss of the supporting buoyancy of water imposed new problems in stability, so that the base of the fore limbs of these amphibians was strengthened by an interclavicle, often of great size, holding the two halves of the shoulder together and forming a braced structure for the articulation of the front limbs. In the pelvic girdle a somewhat similar strengthening is also evident and at least one of the vertebrae has lateral processes and thus shows the beginnning of a sacrum.

Between these anterior and posterior supporting girdles the back became strengthened by the formation, in one way or another, of a vertebral column. Naturally, the limbs, now subjected to new strains and stresses, underwent a more or less rapid development to the typical tetrapod conditions, a matter not so much of differing elements as of different proportions among the basic elements.

The primitive amphibians are usually known as the Labyrinthodontia because of the involved and folded structure of their hollow, conical teeth (Fig. 6).

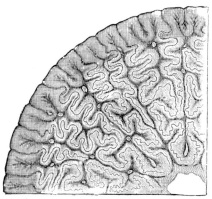

Fig. 6.—A quadrant of a transverse section of a tooth of *Mastodonsaurus giganteus* from Lower Keuper of Württemberg, to show labyrinthine structure.

The Carboniferous Labyrinthodonts, such as *Eogyrinus* and *Palaeogyrinus* mentioned earlier, were not very advanced in their skeleton. The cheek plate was still attached loosely to the skull with which the shoulder girdle was probably also still in connexion. None the less, these amphibia had considerably and perhaps rapidly advanced in size, for *Eogyrinus* was nearly 15 feet long. They were fish-eaters, still inhabitants of the fresh-water swamps and muddy pools characteristic of the Coal Measure period.

The group that includes these genera is known as the Embolomeri, characterized by having vertebrae in which the intercentrum and the pleurocentrum are both thickened discs pierced for the notochord and are set, one behind the other, forming a saddle upon which the neural arch and processes are placed (Fig. 5, c).

17

The Permian amphibians may be typified by *Actinodon** from France, Germany and India; *Eryops** from Texas, Oklahoma and New Mexico in the United States; and *Cacops* from Texas.

Of these, *Eryops* is the largest and the best known because of the many specimens or life-size models in museums. One is exhibited in this museum. It was a large animal, bulky and awkward. An average specimen was just under 7 feet long, the skull being about 20 inches. In shape the skull is rather like a rounded arrow-head with the upper surface depressed. The limbs were bent almost at a right angle when used for walking and were not very large as compared with the size of the animal as a whole. Since the circle of the ribs was incomplete, the animal must have gulped air rather in the manner of a living frog. Amphibians such as *Eryops* probably spent much time out of water, without wandering far from the pools.

Cacops, a much smaller animal of this kind, had a total length of only 16 inches, of which the skull amounted to 5 inches. It was apparently even more terrestrial and had well-developed limbs, the fore feet having only four digits. Correlated with this terrestrial habit and presumably the need for defence against reptilian predators, *Cacops* had small bony plates as armour arranged above the backbone.

These amphibia are classed as Rhachitomi. They too have an anterior intercentrum and a posterior pleurocentrum in each vertebra, but here the former is wedge-shaped, triangular in side view, crescentric as seen from the front, and the pleurocentrum is a rhomboidal bone placed obliquely above and behind the intercentrum. Again they form a saddle on which the neural arch rests, but the whole condition is a more primitive one than that seen in the embolomerous stage (Fig. 5, A). Other Rhachitomi of which the Museum has interesting skulls are *Lydekkerina** and *Deltacephalus.**

During the Carboniferous and Permian there were also living a number of small amphibians that are well known from remains found in England and Western Europe. They are rather like salamanders in appearance but the individuals always have gill supports. For this reason they are known as the "gilled lizards" or Branchiosaurs, but it is now realized that they are the young of rhachitomous forms.

The rhachitomes were struggling more or less successfully to maintain a foothold on the land, but some Permian forms were

* Specimen on exhibition.

PLATE 3

PARACYCLOTOSAURUS

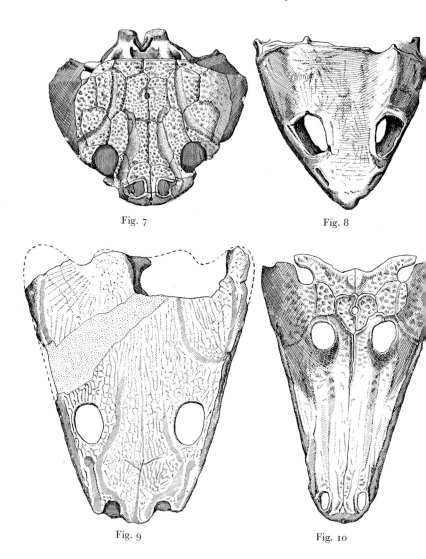

Fig. 7　　　　　　　　　　　Fig. 8

Fig. 9　　　　　　　　　　　Fig. 10

Figs 7, 8, 9, 10.—Skulls of fossil amphibians: *Batrachosuchus* sp. (Trias, S. Africa) (7); *Dvinosaurus secundus* (Upper Permian of Russia) (8); *Metoposaurus diagnosticus* (Keuper of Württemberg) (9); and *Stenotosaurus semiclausus* (Trias of Germany) (10). To show relative proportions of preorbital and postorbital regions, and positions of nostrils. All one-quarter natural size.

already giving up the struggle and returning to the ancestral ways of life.

In the following period, the Trias, there were many amphibia of somewhat similar appearance, such as *Parotosaurus,** *Cyclotosaurus* and *Trematosaurus,* of which numbers of specimens, especially skulls, have been found in Europe. A particularly fine skeleton of *Paracyclotosaurus** nearly 9 feet long, cast from a natural mould discovered in New South Wales, is exhibited in the gallery (Fig. 11; Plate 3). Other related kinds, with interesting skulls, are known from England, South Africa, the United States and the U.S.S.R.

All of these amphibians had abandoned life on the land and had returned to the waters. Most of them lived in fresh-water pools, including that giant of the time, *Mastodonsaurus,** with a skull 4 feet long. Certain long-skulled genera, such as *Aphaneramma,** from the Middle Trias of Spitsbergen, are remarkable for having become marine and thus salt-water living, at least in their adult stages.

These Triassic forms, wherever they are found, are clearly degenerate. Their heads were comparatively large and had the orbits facing upwards; the limbs were feeble and would have been unsuited for walking on the land; even in the water the animals rested mainly upon the great clavicles and interclavicle. The body and tail were often short. The vertebrae show a reduction on the conditions already described for the other amphibian groups. The pleurocentrum was never more than cartilaginous and the inter-centrum is the sole bony support of the neural arch and processes. This condition is known as stereospondylous and these amphibians are consequently often referred to as the Stereospondyli (Fig. 5, B).

These three major groups, the Embolomeri, Rhachitomi and Stereospondyli, contain a numerous and spectacular company, many of which figure in restoration pictures of the Coal Measure age; they are important, but they do not exhaust the amphibian lines of development.

In the Carboniferous there were many small amphibians of quite different appearance having in common a condition of the vertebrae in which the notochord is invested by a bony cylinder or husk, thus suggesting the name Lepospondyli. Some, such as *Dolichosoma* and *Ophiderpeton,* which are found in the Coal Measures of Kilkenny in Eire, had lost their limbs and were shaped like snakes. *Dolichosoma,* the larger of these, was about 3 feet long.

Some of the Lepospondyls still retained legs, though they were very small, and were remarkable for the growth of the skull in its hinder region. In *Diplocaulus*,* for example, the head was shaped like a boomerang, with the eyes near the front and the outer and hinder angles of the skull greatly produced so that the width of the skull was about equal to the length of the whole animal, that is, about 2 feet. It is almost certain that *Diplocaulus* was adapted for living on the lake-bottom like the modern skate on the sea-bed.

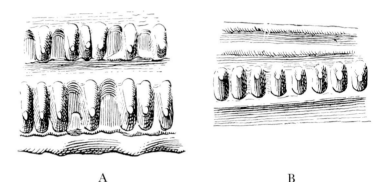

A   B

Fig. 11.—*Paracyclotosaurus.* Arrangement of teeth in upper (A) and lower (B) jaws. Natural size.

Closely related are the small, lizard-like Microsaurs whose first remains were discovered many years ago in decayed tree-stumps of the Coal Measures (L. Penn.) of Joggins, Nova Scotia. The little animals had evidently been trapped within the stumps. One of these Microsaurs was *Hylerpeton*, of which the Museum has several specimens collected by Sir William Dawson, their discoverer.

The Lepospondyls are obviously degenerate and though their skulls are essentially of the Labyrinthodont type their relationship would not seem to be very close. The vertebrae, on the other hand, are like those of the modern salamanders. Salamanders have normal though short limbs, and their limb girdles are cartilaginous. They too are degenerate in their skeletal features. Their geological history is obscure and fossil examples are not known until the Tertiary, the most famous being the Miocene *Andrias*,* one specimen of which was described in 1731 by Johann Jakob Scheuchzer, municipal physician and a canon of Zürich, as the remains of a sinner who had been drowned in the Flood (Fig. 12). That specimen is now in the Teyler Museum in Haarlem, Holland, but a very similar specimen is on exhibition in the Fossil Amphibian Gallery.

Other modern amphibians, the Apoda (or Gymnophiona), which resemble large earthworms superficially and are secondarily adapted for burrowing, may possibly be descended from the Permian *Lysorophus*, which is a Microsaur. No fossil Apoda of any antiquity have been found and the evolutionary connexion is therefore purely presumptive, but the similarity in skull and probable habits is suggestive. *Lysorophus* was water-living, and if its descendants took to burrowing in the banks of the pools the way would be open for the adoption of the habitat of some of the present-day forms.

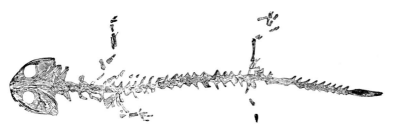

Fig. 12.—*Homo diluvii testis* (man a witness of the deluge); the skeleton of a giant salamander, *Andrias scheuchzeri*, from the Upper Miocene, Oeningen, Baden, Germany. One-tenth natural size.

The frogs and toads, or tailless amphibians, have not changed much since the beginning of the Tertiary. Excellent specimens have been recovered from the Eocene of India, from the Oligocene of Teruel in Spain and from Lower Miocene lignites in the Rhineland. The skeleton of the frog shows remarkable degenerative and adaptive changes, some of which are closely paralleled in the Urodeles (salamanders) but the vertebrae do not have true centra and, indeed, relatively few vertebrae are ever developed, and a number of tail vertebrae are fused together into a spiky mass behind the sacrum. In most of them ribs no longer exist and their place is taken by lengthened transverse processes from the vertebrae.

Until comparatively recently the ancestry of these latest amphibians was obscure, but the series from the present day back to the Jurassic is now clear. Furthermore, two discoveries give a clue to their origin. The first of these was made when a nodule of Triassic age from Madagascar was cracked open revealing the remains of a tailed amphibian which showed little that was frog-like in the skeleton, but in which the skull was quite like that of modern frogs.

23

This amphibian has been named *Protobatrachus*. Another discovery has carried the story back to the Carboniferous, where the small Branchiosaur-like *Amphibamus* and *Miobatrachus*, both of which come from Illinois in the United States, have skulls and skeletons that suggest an early stage in the evolution to the frogs and toads, so that of the comparatively small and unimpressive modern amphibia the frogs and toads can possibly trace their origin to an rhachitomous (i.e. Labyrinthodont) ancestor in the early Carboniferous, while the salamanders have perhaps been derived from the lepospondylous Microsaurs, and thus have an equally ancient but not Labyrinthodont ancestry. There is, however, considerable doubt as to their origin and both groups may have been derived from lepospondyls.

V. THE ORIGIN OF THE REPTILES

There is one considerable omission from the previous section; that of the Seymouriamorpha, a group of Labyrinthodonts containing Carboniferous and Permian forms of great evolutionary significance.

The group takes its name from the small lizard-like amphibian *Seymouria** from the Lower Permian of Seymour, Texas, U.S.A. There is, however, much controversy about the systematic position of this animal, since it has many features in its skeleton that are truly amphibian and at the same time has an equal number of reptilian characters. One determinant, almost impossible of attainment, would be an egg of the animal, for one of the great transitional features must have been the change from an amphibian egg designed for development in the water from which it received its oxygen and nourishment, to that of the first reptile, enclosed in a more or less impermeable shell, and containing a yolk sac, amnion and allantois, and suitable only for development on land. Such an egg contains the water required by the developing young and is known as "cleidoic". The actual steps of this transition will probably never be revealed, for eggs deposited on land are subject to great hazards in fossilization, and the soft parts are most unlikely to be found in any state.

The skeleton of *Seymouria* is about 2 feet in total length. Amphibian characters are seen in the ossification of the skull and in the presence of an intertemporal bone and an otic notch. The skull roof is closely similar to that of the Embolomeres. The teeth are still Labyrinthodont. The short neck shows that the pectoral girdle, which had a long interclavicle, was still in close connexion with the back of the head. The vertebrae, of which the pleurocentrum was the main element, show very little differentiation among themselves. There are signs of lateral line canals, the existence of which would compel a reference to the amphibia.

On the other hand, the shape of the skull, with its closely approximated internal narial openings, and the outwardly directed orbits, are reptilian similarities. There are also an atlas and an axis, wedge-shaped intercentra supporting the pleurocentra, and a sacrum of two vertebrae. Modifications in the shoulder and pelvic girdles suggest well-developed muscles for walking, and both hands and feet have five digits.

25

Whatever its systematic position, features in the skeleton suggest that *Seymouria* is linked to the Anthracosauria through the Carboniferous and Lower Permian *Diplovertebron*, which has also

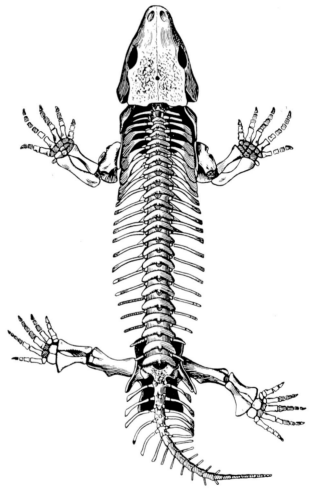

Fig. 13.—*Seymouria* seen from above. About one-quarter natural size. [After Williston.]

the reptilian features of wedge-shaped intercentra, a long-stemmed interclavicle and a five-fingered hand. *Seymouria*, *Diplovertebron* and Anthracosaurs all have a single occipital condyle.

26

The phalanges were arranged in the hand and foot in the reptilian number, 2, 3, 4, 5, 3 (4).

The reptilia as a whole show significant advances on the amphibia. With eggs that could be hatched on the dry land the essential dependence upon the waters had ceased. As with the egg, the adult was suited to a new form of life in a new habitat, so that the skeleton had to become adapted for the support of the body without the aid of any external medium. New habits of life and of feeding brought inevitable changes in the rate of metabolism. The skeletal requirements brought about muscular changes: there were advances in the structure of the vertebrae and limbs and of the muscles that were attached to them. There were changes in the blood supply to these muscles and, co-ordinated with this, changes in the heart and lungs and in the blood-vessels themselves. Correlated with these developments, there was a notable advance in the brain, with the beginnings of a neopallium, the region that receives the stimuli from eyes and ears and from the limbs.

Life was thus entering upon a new, a higher, and certainly a more complex level, but the reptiles were still cold-blooded, subject to the control of external temperature changes, and mentally far below the level of the humblest mammals that we know today.

In many of its features *Seymouria* shows a degree of specialization that would preclude it from the immediate line of reptilian ancestry, despite its strong similarities to both amphibians and reptiles, even if its age were appropriate.

Some authors link *Diadectes*, also from the Lower Permian of Texas, with *Seymouria*. (See p. 30)

VI. PRIMITIVE REPTILES

Whatever may be said of the reptilian characters of the Permian *Seymouria* it is too late in time to be the ancestor of the reptiles, for we have evidence that they were already in being in the late Carboniferous. *Seymouria* probably shares with them a common ancestor in the earlier part of that period.

The most primitive reptiles are included in the Order Cotylosauria. The name means cup-lizards and refers to the shape of the vertebrae. The Order comprises the basal stock of all reptiles, from which a rich and varied progeny was to develop, on land, in the sea and in the air.

COTYLOSAURIA

The most primitive group of the Cotylosauria includes *Gephyrostegus* from the Gas-coal formation of Bohemia, and *Captorhinus* and *Limnoscelis* from the Lower Permian of Texas and New Mexico, U.S.A. This group, probably as near to the main line as any that is known, became extinct in the Middle Permian.

Captorhinus and *Limnoscelis* are well known and reveal in some detail the typical primitive reptilian features. The skull is completely roofed, except for the openings for the nostrils, eyes and the pineal foramen. The otic notch of the Amphibia is lost, to the advantage of the reptile jaw suspension. The skull is more triangular and in profile more rounded than in amphibians, and in the Cotylosaurs varied types of teeth, differing from the amphibian pattern, have already been developed. *Limnoscelis* has a row of sharp teeth in the jaws, but *Captorhinus* has several rows on the infolded maxilla and very small teeth on the pterygoid. The former was probably a flesh-eater and the latter adapted for eating shell-fish.

The vertebrae are cup-shaped with a central cavity for the notochord in the pleurocentra, and with only a small segment of intercentrum, but there is little difference as yet between the various regions of the spinal column.

The shoulder and the pelvic girdles are stronger and more firmly attached to the axial skeleton in view of the new need for bony support, but the limbs, though better proportioned than in most amphibians, were still used awkwardly and stuck out from the sides

28

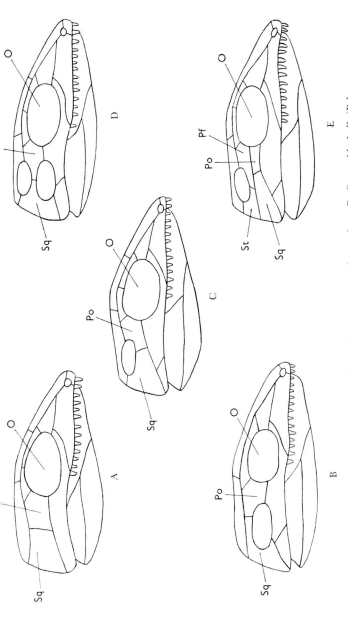

Fig. 14.—Anapsid skull (Cotylosaurs, Chelonia); no temporal opening. B, Synapsid skull (Pelycosaurs, Therapsids); squamosal and postorbital meet above temporal opening. C, Euryapsid skull (Plesiosaurs); squamosal and postorbital meet below temporal opening. D, Diapsid skull (Dinosaurs, Crocodiles and Pterosaurs); two temporal openings between squamosal and postorbital. E, Parapsid skull (Ichthyosaurs); squamosal and postorbital separated from opening by the supratemporal and postfrontal. O, orbit; Pf, postfrontal; Po, postorbital; Sq, squamosal; St, supratemporal.

of the body. A long interclavicle, an expanded ilium and reduced intercentra are true reptilian characters, as is the phalangeal formula of 2.3.4.5.3 for the hand and 2.3.4.5.4 for the foot. *Captorhinus* was about 2 feet in length; *Limnoscelis* about 5 feet.

Most of these features are demonstrated, in an exaggerated form, in another Cotylosaur, *Pareiasaurus* (Plate 4), from the Permian of South Africa and Russia. This is an animal about 9 feet long, with massive limbs and with feet that were specialized.

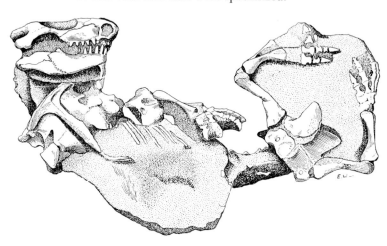

Fig. 15.—Skull and ventral aspect of skeleton of *Procolophon laticeps* from the Karroo of South Africa. Approximately three-quarters natural size.

Pareiasaurus,* as can be seen in the exhibited specimen, has a strongly sculptured skull, the roof and sides of which are walled in by bone, although the pineal opening is rather large. There are teeth on several of the palate bones and their shape and structure suggest that the animal was a vegetarian. The remains of Pareiasaurs have been found in what was apparently once swampy or marshy ground and it is probable that this was their natural habitat.

Another possibly related group is that of the Diadectidae, typified by *Diadectes*, from the Lower Permian of Texas, U.S.A. These animals have skulls curiously specialized and much more must be learned about them.

By the Middle Permian, Pareiasaurs were becoming rare in South Africa, but had appeared in other parts of the world. For example, in addition to notable discoveries made in the north of Russia,

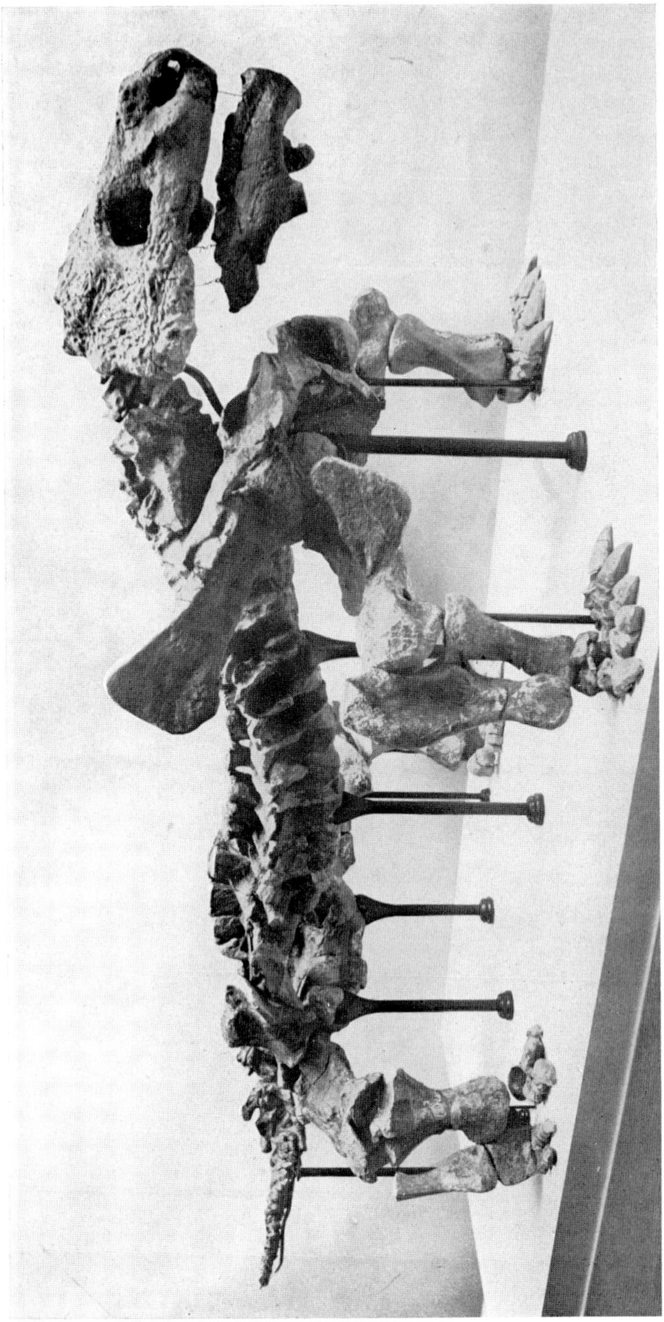

PLATE 4

PAREIASAURUS BAINI

remains of small, peculiarly horned, allied animals have been found in the Permian of north-east Scotland. One of these, *Elginia*, has a characteristically sculptured skull, bearing comparatively large spines (Plate 5). Though *Elginia** was small some other Cotylosaurs were even smaller; for example, *Procolophon** (Fig. 15), from the Trias of South Africa, of which the Museum has a fine collection. In this form the pineal foramen and the orbits are comparatively large, and the skull has no sculpture, but otherwise the skeleton is closely similar to that of its great relation, *Pareiasaurus*.

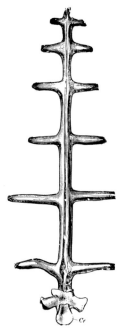

Fig. 16.—Anterior view of the centrum (Ce) and spine with cross pieces of a dorsal vertebra of *Naosaurus claviger*, Permian of Texas. One-sixth natural size.

Fig. 17.—Dorsal vertebra and spine of *Edaphosaurus*. Cf. Fig. 16. One-quarter natural size.

PELYCOSAURIA

Among the ancient groups of reptiles that flourished during the Permian there were the Pelycosauria, derived from a captorhinomorph ancestor. Often of large size, over 10 feet long, they had skulls less completely roofed and high as compared with those of the Cotylosauria, and had massive lower jaws. The vertebrae too are of more advanced type and are remarkable for the length and ornamentation of their neural spines. These were sometimes over 3 feet long and must originally have supported a web of skin. The function of this web has been interpreted in various ways: that it was a secondary sexual character, adorning the males; that it was a sail and of assistance to the movement of the animal if it went swimming; and that it served as a radiator of the heat of the reptile, since the web was probably highly supplied with blood-vessels, or alternatively that it might have absorbed heat from the atmosphere. In *Dimetrodon** the neural spines were simple; in *Naosaurus* and *Edaphosaurus** they had cross pieces of bone arranged on them more or less symmetrically (Figs 16, 17).

The cumbrous *Edaphosaurus* had a number of crushing plates arranged on its palate and was probably a vegetarian.

Dimetrodon, although about the same length as *Edaphosaurus* (about 12 feet), was more slenderly built and may be assumed to have been more active in its habits. This is of some importance, as it appears that a group of very important reptiles, the Therapsida, is descended from the *Dimetrodon*-like Pelycosaurs.

THERAPSIDA

This name Therapsida is translatable as "beast-arches" and bears reference to the mammalian form of the bony arch between the orbit and the openings on the hinder part of the skull (see Fig. 14, B). Other names that have been used for the group are Theromorpha (beast-shaped) and Anomodontia (irregular-toothed) which draw attention to other characteristics.

The group is of particular interest and importance, for it includes among its constituents not only some large reptiles with all the awkwardness of movement and many of the primitive characters of the earliest forms, but also some of the most significant reptiles that we know from these geological periods. These many forms range in time from the Permian to the Trias and occur mainly in

South Africa, although other specimens have been discovered in East Africa, Russia, Scotland, the United States of America, Brazil, India, Indo-China, China, and Antarctica.

DINOCEPHALIA

Some of these reptiles, known as the Dinocephalia or "huge heads", were massive and up to 13 feet long. They had heavy skulls and awkward-looking limbs. The skull still had an opening for the pineal eye. The occipital condyle for the articulation of the skull on the first vertebra of the neck was single. The teeth, on the margins of the jaws only and not upon the palate, indicate that some forms, like *Titanosuchus*, were carnivores, and that others, like *Tapinocephalus*, were herbivorous.

The Dinocephalia, typically developed in the Middle Permian of South Africa, are also known from beds of the same age in Russia.

DICYNODONTIA

A closely related group is that of the Dicynodontia or "double-dog-toothed" reptiles. Some of them were about the size of a rat, but the largest were about 7 feet long. Again, the skull had a pineal foramen and the brain was small and primitive. The skull shows

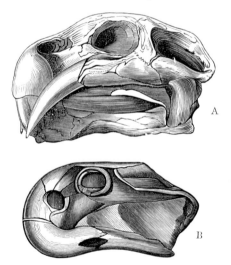

Fig. 18.—Skull and lower jaw of *Dicynodon lacerticeps* (A) and *Aulacocephalodon baini* (B) from the Triassic of South Africa. Left side views; one-third natural size.

interesting differences from the forms so far described: in front there was a toothless beak rather like that of a turtle and the occipital condyle at the back was three-lobed, also rather like that of a chelonian. The importance of the latter feature will be dealt with later under the mammal-like reptiles. In the mouth there were the beginnings of a secondary palate; and though many forms had no teeth at all, others had a pair of large tusks, one on each side of the upper jaw, which grew continuously throughout the life of the animal (Fig. 18).

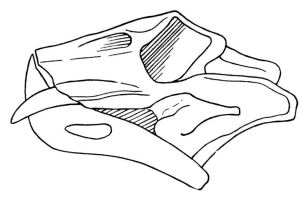

Fig. 19.—Skull of *Lystrosaurus* seen from left side. Note opening of nostrils just in front of orbit. Original from the Karroo of the Orange Free State. One-half natural size.

The decrease of the dentition is interesting, for though some primitive forms had small cheek teeth, most of the Dicynodonts had only the two "tusks", and these seem to have been characteristic of the males, the presumed females being toothless, and the jaws were covered by a horny denture rather like that of the chelonians.

The animals were vegetarians and largely restricted to the marshlands. *Dicynodon** is the typical genus and is well known through hundreds of specimens referred to over seventy species; almost all come from the Karroo of South Africa and bear ample testimony to the remarkable skill and enthusiasm of the palaeontologists of the Union. Dr. Robert Broom was especially prominent in this work. Another interesting and common genus, *Lystrosaurus** (Fig. 19), had a comparatively small skull with a sloping face, and with nostrils just in front of the eyes. Some Lystrosaurs were aquatic and no doubt gained a measure of protection from the carnivorous reptiles by this habit. Certainly all these Dicynodonts disappeared in the later stages of the Trias and may well have been exterminated by the larger flesh-eaters.

Lystrosaurus occurs in Triassic beds in India, Indo-China, in South Africa and in Antarctica; *Dicynodon*, in excellent preservation, is known from the Upper Permian of the North Dvina region of Russia. A large and nearly related form, *Kannemeyeria*, is found in South Africa and Brazil; and all these occurrences show how widespread these animals were during Permian and Triassic times. The finds in Britain have been few, but *Gordonia*, a small reptile with a *Dicynodon*-like skull with tusks, and *Geikia*, a small and toothless animal somewhat like *Lystrosaurus*, have been discovered in the Upper Permain of Morayshire in Scotland.

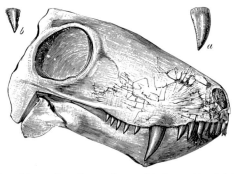

Fig. 20.—Skull and lower jaw (incomplete at hinder ends) of *Aelurosaurus felinus* (a Gorgonopsid) from the Permian of South Africa. Right side view; two-thirds natural size. a, b, two upper teeth, natural size.

THERIODONTIA

Closely related to the Dicynodontia is another important sub-order known as the Theriodontia ("beast-toothed"). For the purposes of this account the Theriodonts can be dealt with as of five groups, all of which had much in common. They were all, for example, lightly built animals, though they varied from the size of a rat to that of a donkey. More important from the evolutionary point of view was the differentiation of their teeth into series very much like those of the mammals we know today. There were incisors, canines, and molars behind the canines. Furthermore, the lower canine was placed in front of the upper as in the mammals. Skull and skeleton both showed advances towards a condition that may be called mammalian.

PLATE 5

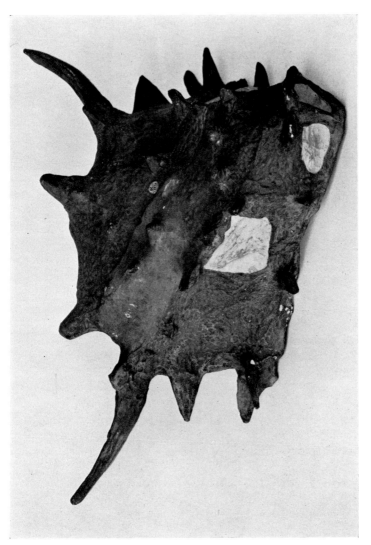

ELGINIA MIRABILIS

Gorgonopsia

These reptiles had usually a long and narrow skull in which a pineal foramen was still developed and on which there was a single occipital condyle. On the palate there were indications that a secondary plate was being developed. The number of teeth in the jaws varied somewhat in the different genera and species, but there were frequently five upper incisors, and five simple teeth behind the canine on each side (Fig. 20). The skeleton shows some advance to a more graceful appearance than the more primitive forms mentioned in earlier sections, but the sternum in the Gorgonopsians was still ossified and the formula for the joints in the fingers and toes was 2.3.4.5.3, the primitive number. *Gorgonops* itself, from which the group takes its name, had a skull about 8 inches long. It was a carnivore like most other Theriodonts.

All these animals are of Permian age and nearly all are from South Africa, although three genera have been recorded from the North Dvina region of Russia.

Therocephalia

These also were carnivores with a skull shaped like that of a dog. Here too the pineal foramen was still open and the occipital condyle was single. The teeth were arranged much as in the Gorgonopsia, but there were three or more pairs of incisors in the upper jaw and there was a series of small and simple teeth behind the canine on each side which might number as many as twelve. The skeleton shows the vestiges of a cleithrum in the shoulder girdle.

Among the Museum specimens of this kind is the very well-preserved skeleton of a fore limb that has been named *Theriodesmus phylarchus**. It is very mammalian in appearance and the ulna has an olecranon process, or funny bone, well developed. Furthermore, the Therocephalian hands and feet have the mammalian number of phalanges, viz. 2.3.3.3.3.

All the forms known are Permian and are mostly from South Africa, though a genus named *Anna* comes from the North Dvina of Russia.

Bauriamorpha

Certain advanced kinds of Therocephalians are classed under the term Bauriamorpha, since the genus *Bauria* is one of the best known of them. For example, in their skulls the pineal foramen, so long persistent in most of the related groups, is either small or absent. In the mouth a secondary palate is developed and the significance of this will be dealt with among other topics in the next section. Their phalanges were disposed in the mammalian number. These forms are all South African also, but they are all of Triassic age.

For the general reader it may seem dull to describe any group of animals merely on certain characters of the skull or skeleton. But on such small but significant details the discussion of one of the greatest events in evolutionary history depends, and that is dealt with in the next chapter, where, in the first place, other groups of the Theriodontia, the Cynodontia and Ictidosauria must be considered.

D

VII. REPTILES AND THE RISE OF MAMMALS

The mammal-like reptiles are of great interest for two reasons. Firstly, they are well known from some excellently preserved specimens. Secondly, if they do not actually show the rise of mammals from reptiles, they at least indicate the lines along which that evolution has taken place. There are problems, as in all discussions on the major pathways of vertebrate evolution. Some of these problems are perhaps insoluble, others have as yet no satisfactory answers. There is, however, no doubt that the particular development we must consider here finds its immediate origin in the Cynodonts.

Cynodontia

The Cynodonts can be summarily described as dog-shaped animals with a dog-like dentition. This description is fairly true if one bears in mind a rather long-bodied, short-legged dog, with a long and heavy tail. Some were only a foot or so long, but *Cynognathus*,* which is represented in the Museum by several specimens, was about 7 feet long (Plate 6).

On top of the skull, the pineal foramen, as in the Bauriamorphs, was small or had disappeared. At the back of the skull the occipital condyle was tripartite or double (as in *Cynognathus*) (Fig. 21). The

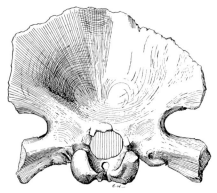

Fig. 21.—Back of skull of a mammal-like reptile, showing the development of two articular condyles from the occipital bone. The opening above is the foramen magnum for the issue of the spinal cord. One-half natural size.

40

PLATE 6

CYNOGNATHUS

teeth were differentiated, as in other Theriodonts, into incisors, canines and molars. The upper jaw-bones (maxillae) and the palatine bones together formed a roof or secondary palate above which the nostril openings communicated with the back of the mouth. The secondary palate thus formed is a mammalian feature to enable the animal to eat and breathe at the same time. The usual reptilian habit of gulping air and food spasmodically and intermittently is not possible in a mammal whose warm-blooded metabolism demands a continuous supply of air to the lungs.

Whether or not any of the Cynodonts were warm-blooded and consequently had a warm covering on or under the skin is impossible to say. The females were probably egg-laying, and this is also true of the Monotremes, a primitive sub-class of mammals. Undoubtedly they were active animals and this may have been largely responsible for their evolutionary progress.

*Cynognathus crateronotus,** from the Lower Trias of South Africa, shows most of the features enumerated above, though its limbs are unfortunately not preserved. Its skull has a small pineal opening, and a double condyle at the back.

Many years ago, when it was noticed that living amphibia and mammals had a double condylar articulation and that most of the living reptiles had a single one, it was assumed that mammals must have evolved directly from amphibians. The study of the Therapsida shows that the double condyle of these fossils is derived from the breaking up into flanges of the single occipital condyle. Apart from the trefoil condition in the Chelonia, this separation into two or more flanges is unique in reptiles.

Tooth differentiation is on the mammalian plan. *Cynognathus* has on each side four incisors, one canine, five premolars and four molars. The post-canine teeth (cheek-teeth) all have several cusps. The lower teeth in biting were on the inner side of the upper teeth. All the teeth are serrated and it is obvious that the animal was a carnivore.

It has been suggested that the mammalian resemblances of the teeth are superficial and that the teeth were not replaced in the mammalian way. Normally, in reptiles the succession of teeth is continuous, new teeth replacing discarded ones—the polyphyodont condition. In mammals there are two series only, a juvenile or milk dentition and an adult dentition, that is, a diphyodont condition.

It is difficult to tell which condition existed in the advanced Cynodonts, but recent investigations with X-rays show that the mode of implantation of the teeth and their developing stages, so far as they can be observed, are analogous in some ways to those of mammals.

Much of the skeleton of *Cynognathus* is truly reptilian, but there are advanced features. The vertebrae are biconcave but without intercentra, though double-headed ribs occur from the neck to the beginning of the tail. Both shoulder and hip girdles show an advance, principally in response to the new muscular demands of the limbs; for in the limbs the old, outwardly directed "elbow" and "knee" had been rearranged. The elbow was now bent back and the knee bent forward as in the dog. The sprawling attitude was thus directed differently and with far more possibility of extension of the limb and therefore of increase of speed. The digits of the hand and foot, however, had the phalanges arranged on the reptilian plan of 2.3.4.5.3, though some of those in the third and fourth digits were small in size.

The Cynodonts thus exhibit a mixture of Gorgonopsian and Therocephalian features and descent has been argued from both. Considering only the skull characters, the Therocephalia and the Bauriomorpha would seem to form a better basis, but on the structure of the limbs the descent would appear to be more clearly related to the Gorgonopsians. In this respect vestigial, rather than incipient, features are more revealing and the development of a partial secondary palate was probably accomplished more than once.

Ictidosauria

Cynodont evolution is of exceptional interest, for although *Cynognathus* was a Lower Triassic Cynodont, a series of small but advanced forms with many similar features occurs in the Upper Triassic of South Africa. This little group is known as the Ictidosauria and its most characteristic members are small creatures with skulls about an inch long. Some of these are remarkably mammalian in appearance. In them, as in other Theriodonts already mentioned, the pineal foramen is closed and a secondary palate of efficient construction has been established. Further, the bar of bone (postorbital bar) behind the eye has been lost so that the characteristically reptilian ring of bones around the orbit is broken, leaving the open mammalian condition of the temporal fossa.

More important in a way are the articular relations between the lower and the upper jaws. Throughout the class Reptilia a series of bones normally contributes to the hinder part of the lower jaw, and of them the articular bone rocks or swings upon the quadrate bone in the skull. In the mammals the lower jaw consists entirely of the dentary, an upwardly directed part of which articulates with the squamosal bone of the skull. In the Ictidosauria the reptilian lower jaw has lost many of its constituent parts but the dentary-articular joint is still there. However it seems that a contact between the squamosal and the dentary also exists in *Diarthrosaurus* ("double joint reptile") of South Africa. This must be on the Reptile-Mammalian border line.

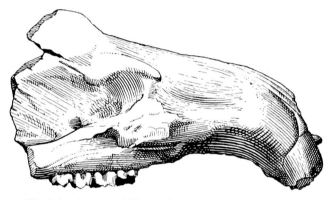

Fig. 22.—*Tritylodon*. A mammal-like reptile; incomplete skull seen from right side showing molar teeth. Trias of South Africa. Natural size.

Several remarkable skulls are known which seem to have almost entirely mammalian characters, and one of these, *Tritylodon*,* was long considered to be a mammal (Figs. 22, 23). The original specimen, exhibited in the Fossil Reptile Gallery, comes from the Upper Triassic of South Africa. Several skulls and skeletons of a form near to *Tritylodon* have been discovered in Northern Arizona. Similar kinds of animals are *Bienotherium* from China and *Oligo-kyphus** from the Liassic of England. Though their teeth are specialized and bear close similarity to those of the multituberculate mammals, their lower jaws show traces cf the old reptilian hinge, so that these advanced and almost mammalian animals must still be classified as reptiles.

By the end of the Trias only these forms were in evidence: the less advanced Therapsids had left the field. The oldest known mammals are also of Upper Triassic age and come from England and South Africa. The significant changes in the physiology of the vertebrates may have occurred gradually within the Therapsids themselves. The most recent evidence shows that these advanced

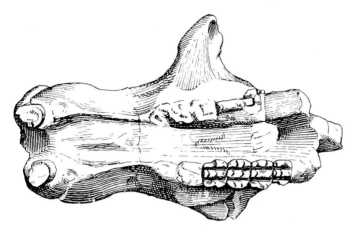

Fig. 23.—*Tritylodon.* Palatal view showing tusks and grooved molars. Natural size.

Tritylodonts could lie down like a dog—a very unreptilian posture but one associated with the vertebral movements needed when fur is licked. Their ribs show that rhythmic breathing was possible. Were then the animals warm-blooded and hairy? In the absence of soft parts one cannot be sure. From the hard parts it is clear that the time must have been one of experiment, though whether the mammals arose from a single source or from several collateral and closely allied sources has yet to be established.

VIII. CHELONIA

The Chelonia are among the best known of living reptiles. They are widespread in distribution, either naturally or as pets, and are grotesque in appearance. The enclosure of the body, parts of the limbs, and in certain circumstances the head, neck and tail, within a bony shell is unique in living reptiles and uncommon in the vertebrates of today. None the less, certain forms of the dinosaurs, which are dealt with later, approach this condition and *Glyptodon* among fossil mammals and the living armadillo are superficially similar. On examination the remarkable features of the Chelonia can be related to fundamental reptilian traits. If no complete ancestral line for their origin from primitive reptiles is available in the fossil record, at least a strong indication of its probable direction can now be given.

The shell of the turtles and tortoises is known as the carapace in its upper part and the plastron in its lower, abdominal, portion. Both of these shells have intimate relationship with the skeleton; both are bony and are overlain in life by a horny covering whose pattern does not coincide with that of the bony shell, but which, even in the fossil, can usually be traced upon it. The carapace is underlain by the expanded ribs.

In the modern chelonians, the upper parts of the limbs are within the shell and the head and neck can be retracted. Where the head is withdrawn by a sideways movement of the neck, the Chelonia are classed as Pleurodira; if the withdrawal is by a vertical movement of the neck, they are called Cryptodira.

The skull itself is usually completely roofed. The pineal foramen is closed; the orbits and external nostrils are, of course, open, but there are no temporal openings in the real sense and these animals can be classed as without arches, that is, Anapsid. It is true that in some forms, as in the large fossil *Archelon**, there are openings in the cheek region, but these are not true temporal openings, and are fissures developed through reduction of bone. The chelonian skull has some features in common with that of Diadectids but a direct relationship is not likely.

All living, and with one exception all fossil, forms of Chelonia are toothless, and a remarkable bony denture is developed in the

46

jaws. The occipital condyle is tripartite; this is probably related to the movements during retraction of the head and neck. The neck itself is composed of eight vertebrae, usually of complicated structure to permit the necessary bending in retraction. The shoulder girdle is triradiate and is without a trace of the clavicle or interclavicle, but the remnants of these bones are discernible in the epiplastra and in the entoplastron respectively of the plastron.

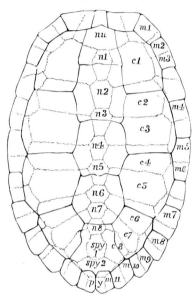

Fig. 24.—Carapace of a tortoise, *Hardella thurgi*, from the Pliocene of the Siwalik Hills, India; the wavy lines are the divisions between the bones, the firm ones those between the overlying horny shields, c 1–8, costal bones; m 1–11, marginal bones; n 1–8, neural bones; nu, nuchal bone; py, pygal bone; spy, 1, 2, suprapygal bones. [After Lydekker.]

The vertebrae of the trunk are ten in number and all of these, except the first, are in contact with the carapace; in the course of chelonian history the number of dorsal vertebrae has been reduced. There are two sacrals.

The carapace in all Chelonia has practically the same elements. There is a medium row of eight neural bones, in contact below with the neural processes of the second to ninth dorsals, and in front of them is a nuchal and sometimes a postnuchal, and at their hinder end is one and occasionally two pygals and suprapygals. On either side of the neurals are eight costals. This number is normal and the costals

47

are always fused with the dorsal ribs of vertebrae 2–9. These plates are dermal in origin and are homologous with the dorsal scutes of crocodiles. On the outer side of the costals is an edge of marginals, which may vary in width considerably in the different genera.

The under shell or plastron is of a less standard nature. From front to back it consists of paired epiplastra (remnants of the clavicles)

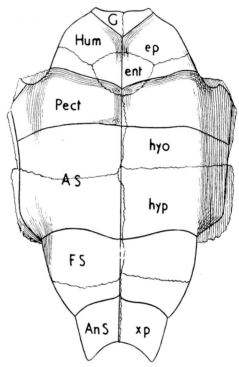

Fig. 25.—Chelonian plastron or under shield, *Ocadia crassa*. Bones are ep, epiplastron; ent, entoplastron; hyo, hyoplastron; hyp, hypoplastron; xp, xiphiplastron. Epidermal shields are G, gular; Hum, humeral; Pect, pectoral; AS, abdominal; FS, femoral; AnS, anal.

around an unpaired entoplastron (representing the interclavicle), followed by paired hyoplastra, then in some forms only, mesoplastra, then usually hypoplastra, and at the hinder end, the paired xiphiplastra. This plastron is sometimes, as in the tortoises, complete, but in some of the marine forms it has been greatly reduced. It is thought by some that the plastron elements have been derived from abdominal ribs in the ancestral form, but there is good reason for thinking that, like the carapace elements, they originated from paired scutes.

The two portions of the shell are connected in the middle of the sides by what is known as the "bridge". The shell is open in front for the head and neck, and at the back for the tail and the hinder projection of the legs in walking.

The limbs are widely spaced and the living chelonian straddles its way along in a somewhat Cotylosaurian manner. The limbs themselves have Cotylosaurian characters, but they are also specialized, and there is a remarkable trend towards the reduction of the number of the joints in hands and feet, the mammalian number of these, 2.3.3.3.3, being the maximum in the Chelonia. These phalanges vary, however, in length and in some marine forms are quite long.

The character of the skull with its anapsid features and the nature of the limbs all suggest Cotylosaurian (perhaps Procolophonid) relationships for the Chelonia. The first chelonian, *Triassochelys*, from the Keuper of Germany, was land-living and had already a well-developed shell. It is unique in having teeth, though they are restricted to the palate and were absent on the jaws.

EUNOTOSAURIA

It was long thought that there existed a complete gap in the developmental series between the Permian Cotylosauria and the Upper Triassic Chelonia. Yet so long ago as 1914, D. M. S. Watson had fully described *Eunotosaurus*,* from the Middle Permain of South Africa, represented in the Museum collection by five specimens, which appears to fill the gap and helps to explain much that otherwise is difficult to understand. The withdrawal, for example, of the shoulder girdle within the shell and the diminution of the number of dorsal vertebrae, suggest that the ancestor must have had a narrow shoulder region which could gradually be shifted back. If the ancestor were like *Eunotosaurus* there is little difficulty in visualizing the process. The available material shows the palatal aspect of the skull and the dorsal region of the body. There are teeth on the palate; the neck is long and flexible; there are ten dorsal vertebrae and eight of them have remarkable, leaf-like ribs (Fig. 26). There is a thin armour of bony scutes on the back. The position of the neural arch on the centra is also suggestive of the chelonian condition. Anteriorly, the shoulder girdle has clavicles and an

49

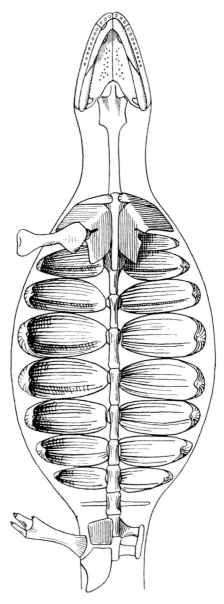

Fig. 26.—*Eunotosaurus*, a possible ancestor of the Chelonia. Restored skeleton seen from below, showing the expanded and leaf-like ribs. [After D. M. S. Watson.]

interclavicle that are all clearly part of the functional girdle, and the girdle as a whole is overlapped dorsally by the first pair of dorsal ribs.

Several specimens of *Eunotosaurus* have just been discovered, so that a reconsideration of its position will be possible, but there can be no doubt that it indicates one way in which a Procolophonid member of the Cotylosauria could have developed into a primitive chelonian. On the other hand, the similarities may be due to parallel development.

Eunotosaurus is accepted by some modern authorities as the most primitive member of the Order and is placed in a sub-order by itself —the Eunotosauria. Generally, however, the Order Chelonia may be divided into three sub-orders. I, the Amphichelydia, represented from the Trias to the Pleistocene; II, the Pleurodira, from Upper Cretaceous to the present; and III, the Cryptodira (including the Trionychidae) from the Jurassic to the present time.

AMPHICHELYDIA

This group includes *Triassochelys* and other primitive genera in which the head was not retracted into the shell. The shell was complete and there were accessory dermal shields on the plastron. The pelvic girdle was in contact with both the carapace and the plastron, though it was still not united with the latter. *Triassochelys* and *Proganochelys*, which both come from the Keuper of Germany, were land tortoises with shells just over 2 feet long. In England there are many Amphichelyds from the Upper Jurassic and the Cretaceous, *Pleurosternon** from the Purbeck Beds of Swanage being the best-known genus. These were water tortoises with a much flatter shell than that in *Triassochelys*. In the skeleton the cervical vertebrae had lost their ribs though the vertebrae were still somewhat biconcave. *Tretosternon,** from the Purbeck and Wealden of England, was somewhat similar, but had a very characteristic tuberculated shell. The Museum has exellent examples of the related form *Platychelys* from the Lithographic Stone of Bavaria as well as from England. There are also numerous good skulls of *Rhinochelys,** each an inch or so long, which are not uncommon in the Cambridge Greensand (Cretaceous).

In the sub-order there should perhaps be included the marine Thalassemydidae, in which the shell was incompletely developed and in which the feet were clawed and perhaps webbed, so that some of these animals may have been adapted for life on land as well as in the sea. The Plesiochelydae, in contrast, had thick shells and the phalanges were sometimes reduced in number and size. *Plesiochelys** itself, from the Upper Jurassic of Germany, Switzerland and France and from the Wealden of England, had a thick vaulted shell about 12 inches long.

The most unusual members of the sub-order Amphichelydia are *Niolamia* which has been found in the Cretaceous of Argentina; and *Meiolania** from the Pleistocene of Australia, of Lord Howe Island, which is 300 miles east-north-east of Sydney, and of Walpole Island, 100 miles south-west of New Caledonia. *Meiolania* is represented in the Museum by the material originally described by Richard Owen (Plate 7). It had a thick, horned skull, nearly 2 feet broad, and the tail was encased in bone like that of the South American armadillo-like mammal *Glyptodon*.

PLEURODIRA

This sub-order includes essentially the families Pelomedusidae and Chelidae. The former are Tertiary to Recent in age and the latter extend in time from the Wealden to the present. These are all turtles in which the head is retracted through a sideways movement of the neck. The skull shows the loss of certain facial bones (nasals and lachrymals) and the pelvic girdle is fused to the carapace and the plastron. The best-known fossils of the group belong to *Podocnemis*, which is found in the London Clay and in younger deposits in North and East Africa. Other genera are known from France, Belgium and the United States, but modern species are confined to the warmer regions of the Southern Hemisphere. This is a chelonian example of the persistence in warmer regions of rather primitive forms that have died out elsewhere.

CRYPTODIRA

There is no doubt that this sub-order contains the most advanced members of the Order, as it also contains by far the most numerous and most widely spread genera. In these the head is withdrawn by the vertical movement of the neck vertebrae and in the land and fresh-water forms the head is completely taken into the shell. The pelvis is not fused with the carapace or plastron.

The fossil record extends from the Jurassic to the present day and the earliest forms are apparently intermediate in character between the Amphychelydia and the later true Cryptodira. The

PLATE 7

A. NIOLAMIA ARGENTINA

B. MEIOLANIA OWENI

last named came in during the Cretaceous and since then they have populated the lands and invaded the fresh waters and some of the seas in the Northern Hemisphere. The amphibious turtles and terrapins date from the Lower Cretaceous and are characterized by a flattened shell that is complete in carapace and plastron. Tortoises

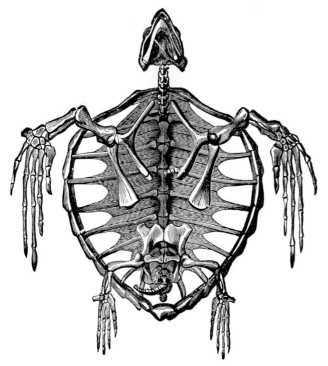

Fig. 27.—Lower view of the skeleton, with plastron removed, of *Caretta caretta*, the Logger-head Turtle. About one-tenth natural size.

often of large size, and generally typified by a rounded or vaulted carapace, are known from the early Tertiary onwards. Thanks to its expeditions and the travels of its staff the Museum has a good collection of many of these forms. For example, there are the almost complete shells of *Testudo ammon* from the Upper Eocene of Egypt and of the larger *Testudo grandidieri** from cavern deposits of Madagascar. The largest tortoise so far discovered is represented by fragments and a restored model of the shell of *Testudo (Colosso-chelys) atlas** from the Lower Pliocene of the Siwalik Hills in India.

The restored model is nearly 8 feet long. These great tortoises were all vegetarians.

The last native tortoise in England was *Emys orbicularis*. Its shells are occasionally found in the eastern counties and it is still to be found alive in Southern Europe.

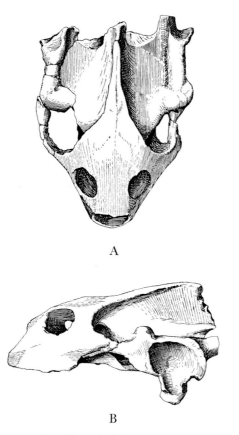

A

B

Fig. 28.—*Trionyx gangeticus*. Type skull from Pleistocene of India. A, upper aspect; B, left side view. Both approximately one-half natural size.

Among the older genera, numerous remains have been found fossil in England. *Chelone benstedi*, for example, occurs in the Chalk, and a leathery turtle, *Eosphargis gigas*, has been found in the London Clay of Sheppey. Smaller forms of true turtles, such as *Argillochelys*,* are not uncommon in the same formation.

55

E

Among large sea turtles is *Allopleuron hoffmanni** from the Upper
Cretaceous of Maastricht in Holland, of which parts of a carapace
are exhibited.

The three-clawed mud-turtles (Trionychidae) appear with all
their typical characters in the Eocene of Europe and the United
States. Well-preserved shells and other remains of *Trionyx** are
found in the London Clay of Sheppey and the Upper Eocene of
Hampshire.

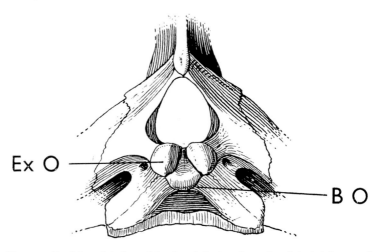

Fig. 29.—Trefoil occipital condyle of a chelonian, formed mainly by the exocci-
pitals—an unusual arrangement in reptiles. BO=basioccipital; ExO=exoccipital.

IX. PLESIOSAURS AND ICHTHYOSAURS

Even by Triassic times some important groups of the reptiles were drifting back to the aquatic habitat of their Amphibian ancestors and the most noteworthy of these are the Sauropterygia (Nothosaurs, Placodonts and Plesiosaurs) and the Ichthyopterygia (Ichthyosaurs). Each of these had a terrestrial ancestor of typically reptilian appearance with a characteristically land-reptile skeleton, so that when they went to sea they did so only by readapting their structure to the demands of aquatic life and not by recapturing the primitive structures that their ancestors once had. The process is not, of course, confined to reptiles or to animals of the past. The whales, seals and dolphins are mammals that have become suitably readapted to a wholly aquatic existence.

In these two great groups of fossil reptiles there were differences in the method and the degree of readaptation and there are also differences as to the extent to which their ancestry is known. Of the two, the Plesiosaurs are the more typically reptilian in appearance.

The Order Sauropterygia includes the Nothosaurs, Placodonts and Plesiosaurs in the strict sense, all of which have some under-lying skeletal similarities. There is, for example, an upper temporal opening on each side of the top of the skull and there is no quadrato-jugal. The pineal opening is present, not as a secondary feature but as one that had never been lost. In most members of the Order the external nostrils had been moved back towards the front of the eye—an aquatic adaptation frequently seen in fossil reptiles. There was no secondary palate, but the pterygoids had grown across and forwards to form with the palatines a roof that served something of the same purpose.

In the skeleton the vertebrae were flat ended or slightly cupped; the ribs of the neck region were double headed, but those of the trunk had only a single head. There was a series of abdominal ribs closely intermeshed. The limb girdles show a tendency towards reduction of the upper (dorsal) elements whereas the lower are long and expanded. As will be seen later, there were significant differences in the limbs of the various Sauropterygians. The Nothosaurs and Placodonts had limbs suitable for use on land or in the water, whereas the more advanced Plesiosaurs had paddles which could not have been of great service on land.

Nothosaurs and Placodonts are of Triassic age, and Plesiosaurs, although their remains do occur in Rhaetic beds, are characteristic of the Jurassic and the Cretaceous.

Certain features indicate that the Nothosaurs cannot be the direct ancestors of the Plesiosaurs. If one examines the series it appears that only the Protorosaurs suggest the possibility of development into Sauropterygians. These are an offshoot of the Cotylosaurs.

It has been suggested in previous editions of this work that *Araeoscelis*, of which the museum has no specimen, may be a typical representative of the Protorosaurs. Very recent work has cast grave doubt on this group, for *Araeoscelis* has been associated with some poorly known genera mainly on its possession of an upper temporal opening, and the nature of this region in the associated genera, *Protorosaurus*, *Trachelosaurus* and *Tanystropheus*, is in fact, unknown. Whether they are related to one another or to *Araeoscelis* remains problematical, as must their alleged relationship with the ancestors of the sauropterygians which rested on the supposition that they had an upper temporal opening.

Araeoscelis comes from the Lower Permian of Texas, but the highly interesting forms, *Tanystropheus* and *Trachelosaurus* are from the Middle and Lower Trias respectively of Switzerland and are thus too late to be ancestors of a group well established in the same Trias. They may, however, be offshoots from the main evolutionary line that share some of the anatomical features of the Sauropterygia.

The Nothosaurs are known best from the Middle Triassic of Europe, especially from Switzerland and North Italy, where the splendid work of Professors Broili and Peyer has done much to reveal the detailed structure of the fossils. Several genera are known, but in superficial appearance they are much alike. Typical Nothosuar bones have also been described from Israel, Jordan and Japan.

They are in general small and graceful creatures with rather acutely triangular skulls. The neck is not quite so long as the body and the tail is often as long as both neck and body together. The skull of many of them is about an inch long and the whole animal may be under a foot in length, or at most twice this size. The more complete specimens suggest a slender and active animal with delicate limbs. There are five fingers and toes, each a little lengthened, and still separate, although there is evidence (especially from one fine specimen from Cheshire in the Museum collection) that the digits were connected by a web of skin. The animals were therefore able to swim though the limbs retained their adaptation for movement over the land. *Nothosaurus* itself was a much larger animal with a skull up to a foot long.

The Museum has a fine collection of such genera as *Nothosaurus,** *Lariosaurus** (Fig. 30), *Ceresiosaurus* and *Pachypleurosaurus.**

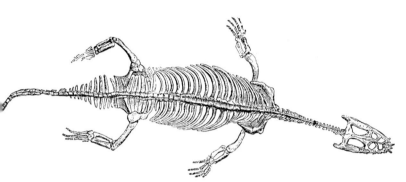

Fig. 30.—Skeleton of a primitive Sauropterygian, *Lariosaurus balsami*, from the Trias of North Italy.

The Placodonts, another group of Triassic Sauropterygians known from European deposits, were fundamentally similar to the Nothosaurs, and like them amphibious, but the former were very different in appearance, being large animals with both the neck and the tail shorter than the body. Within the skull, the palate and the margins of the jaws bore teeth of a kind that does not occur in any other reptiles, although they are somewhat similar to the teeth of some fishes. These teeth, which have quadrilateral bases and rounded, high or dome-like surfaces, were obviously intended for crushing molluscs, and the principal features of the skulls are adaptations to this end. To crush shell-fish in the jaws demands considerable strength in the jaw muscles and this in turn requires jaws and upper skull bones of corresponding size and efficiency. *Placodus* itself has a skull about 9 inches long; in *Cyamodus* (Fig. 31) it was over 8 inches long; and in both of these genera the lower jaw has developed an

59

ascending coronoid process to aid the muscular jaw power. This feature is unusual in reptiles, though it is developed in some mammal-like reptiles and in the mammals.

The shape of the mouth also appears to be adapted for dealing with shell-fish. In *Placochelys*, for example, the front of the mouth

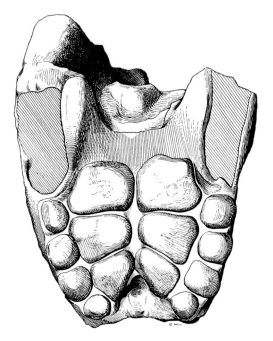

Fig. 31.—*Cyamodus laticeps*, Trias of Bayreuth, Germany. Palate with crushing teeth. One-half natural size.

was narrowed and toothless, serving as a pincer-like organ for picking up the food that was crushed in the hinder teeth. *Henodus* became almost completely toothless and presumably its jaws were covered by a horny layer, or secondary denture, rather like that of the chelonians. Indeed, the similarity does not stop there, for in both of these genera considerable external armour largely enclosed the body, though the armour was composed of a mosaic of small plates rather than the few and readily identifiable plates of Chelonia. All the Placodonts had some armour on the body, both above and below, and this provides another instance of the reptilian potentiality for developing dermal armour.

The placodont armour has suggested to some students a near relationship with the turtles, but it is more probably an example of convergence, that is, an increasing similarity in appearance between dissimilar groups living the same kind of life in the same sort of habitat.

The Plesiosaurs first appear in the Rhaetic, at the close of the Triassic. They were very well developed in the Jurassic, reaching a remarkable degree of profusion in the Lias, and the Museum collection on the walls of the Fossil Reptile Gallery is the finest in the world.

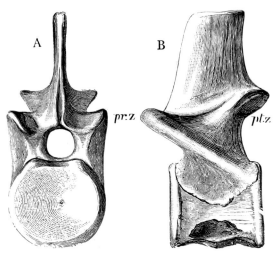

Fig. 32.—Hinder neck vertebra of *Plesiosaurus*, front (A) and left side (B) views. From Lower Lias, Lyme Regis. Two-thirds natural size. pr.z, prezygapophysis; pt.z., postzygapophysis.

In their skull characters they show many features, such as the nares near to the orbits, the presence of a pineal opening and the absence of a quadrato-jugal, that we have encountered in the Nothosaurs. The strong, pointed and striated teeth were confined to the margins of the jaws and there was none on the palate. The jaws were thus admirably adapted to the capture of fish and cuttle-fish and the mouth formed an efficient fish-trap.

Some Plesiosaurs had small, rather triangular skulls on a long neck. In other kinds, the skull was long and on a comparatively short neck. In most cases the body was broad, somewhat flattened, and protected above and below with a series of ribs. The tail was always short. The classic description by Dean Buckland of Oxford was that a Plesiosaur resembled "a snake threaded through the shell of a turtle". There is more in this than a mere superficial resemblance, for the long reptilian limbs were modified for movement in the water by the lengthening of the fingers, which became a string of bony bobbins. In life the paddles were covered with a stiff skin, so that they resembled the turtle flipper and must have

Fig. 33.—Dorsal vetrebra of *Plesiosaurus*, left side view. One-half natural size.

been moved in much the same way. The body of the animal was rowed over the surface of the sea, the limbs acting as oars that could be pulled, backed and even feathered. These features are shown by *Macroplata** from the Lower Lias of Warwickshire (Plate 8).

The speed through the water could not have been great, but the neck allowed darting movements to be made in pursuit of the prey. Smooth pebbles found in Plesiosaur stomach contents show that "stomach-stones", or gastroliths, were swallowed and were no doubt used to help to grind up the harder parts of the food. Remains of fish and the hooks of cuttle-fish, such as *Geoteuthis*, are also found in the stomach contents.

Plesiosaurs varied considerably in size and some were over 40 feet long. The genus *Plesiosaurus** is restricted to the Lower and Upper

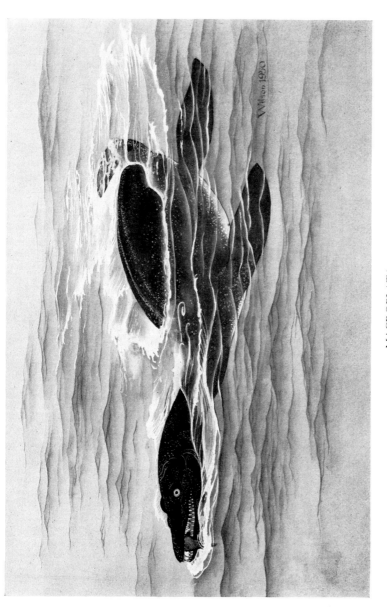

MACROPLATA

Lias of the Jurassic. Lyme Regis in Dorset, Street in Somerset, parts of Leicestershire and Warwickshire have all yielded rich collections, some of the skeletons being remarkably well preserved. The study of these reveals many interesting modifications, especially in the shape and arrangement of the flattened coracoids which form a great buckler in the chest. There are many Liassic species, and the first associated bones, forming an almost complete skeleton, were found by Mary Anning near Lyme Regis in 1821. The specimen was named and described by Dean Conybeare in 1821,

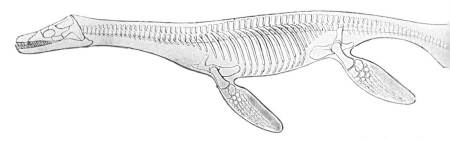

Fig. 34.—Skeleton of *Plesiosaurus macrocepahlus*, from the Lower Lias of Lyme Regis, with outline shading of supposed body line and tail fin. About one-eighteenth natural size.

and is exhibited on the south wall of the Fossil Reptile Gallery. A portrait of Mary Anning hangs on the same wall, and as a memorial to her many discoveries a window was dedicated to her memory in Lyme Parish Church.

In the later stages of the Jurassic and also of the Cretaceous there was a tendency for the Plesiosaurs to attain great size. The related group of the Pliosaurs, for example, had enormous skulls, even up to 6 feet in length, but they had short necks, so that the overall length of these apparent giants did not greatly exceed the larger of the true Plesiosaurs. Apart from their geological age and the relative sizes of their skulls and necks, there were no profound differences in the skeletons. The Museum has a splendid collection, some of it exhibited, due to the long and distinguished labours of Mr. Alfred N. Leeds and his family who studied exhaustively the Oxford Clay brick pits of the Peterborough district.

Kronosaurus of the Lower Cretaceous of Australia, with a skull 10 feet long, was a member of an allied group of which the English *Polyptychodon* is known by numerous teeth (Fig. 36).

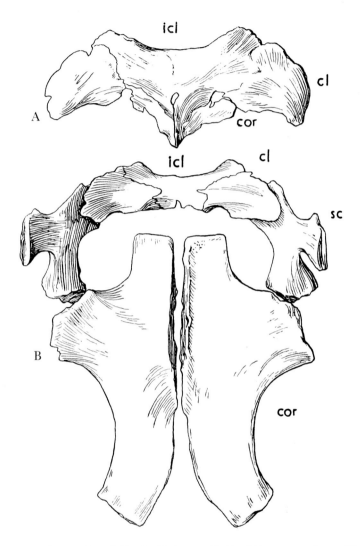

Fig. 35.—The shoulder girdle of a Plesiosaur. B, *Eurycleidus arcuatus*, Lower Lias of Street, seen from above: cor, coracoid; sc, scapula; cl, clavicle; icl, interclavicle. Above is the clavicular arch (A) of *Eurycleidus megacephalus*, seen from below. Both figures about one-sixth natural size. [After Andrews.]

The Leeds collection also revealed complete skeletons of another group of Plesiosaurs, the Elasmosaurs. In England, in the Oxford Clay, such genera as *Cryptocleidus** (Plate 9) and its near relatives (*Picrocleidus** and *Tricleidus**) have been found as fragments and have been painstakingly and accurately restored. They and the Wealden *Leptocleidus* are representatives of a group of small-headed and very long-necked Plesiosaurs that culminated during the Cretaceous, especially in the United States, in fantastic creatures with necks

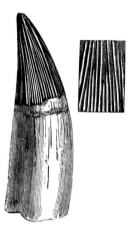

Fig. 36.—Tooth of *Polyptychodon interruptus*, from the Cambridge Greensand; one-half natural size. Part of the ribbed enamel of the crown is shown, natural size, to the right.

over 20 feet long, and with as many as seventy-six cervical vertebrae (*Elasmosaurus*). These necks are believed to have been remarkably flexible.

Although English and American Plesiosaurs have been almost exclusively mentioned so far, remains are known from a wide range of localities in Belgium, France, Germany, India, South Africa and Australia. Although the female Plesiosaurs laid eggs upon the shore and were thus in some measure tied to the land, the group was successfully adapted to a marine life and its members were distributed throughout the world during the later Mesozoic.

The name *Plesiosaurus* means in Greek "nearer to a lizard", and it is undoubtedly apt when compared with the next great group of marine reptiles, the Ichthyosauria, or "fish-lizards", whose appearance gives little clue to their ancestry and reptilian affinities.

66

Like the Plesiosaurs they had a world-wide range; they appeared early in the Triassic and lasted until late in the Cretaceous.

The ancestry of the Ichthyosaurs, at least in its earlier stages, is still a matter for speculation. As will be seen, this group is highly specialized, springing from some terrestrial type not later than the Permian. It has been suggested that a probable ancestor of the

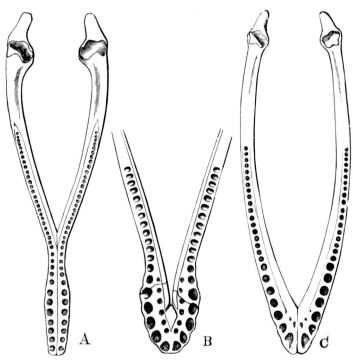

Fig. 37.—Lower jaws, without teeth, seen from above. A, *Peloneustes philarchus*, Oxford Clay of Peterborough; one-eighth natural size. B, *Thaumatosaurus indicus*, Upper Jurassic of India; one-seventh natural size. C, *Plesiosaurus dolichodeirus*, Lower Lias of Lyme Regis; one-quarter natural size.

group might be found in the precursors of a certain Pelycosaur, *Ophiacodon*, which was a long-snouted semi-aquatic animal of the Permian, but Ophiacodont Pelycosaurs have recently been found in Middle Pennsylvanian lycopod stumps at Florence, Nova Scotia, indicating an earlier separation.

The Triassic Ichthyosaurs were also widely distributed; North Italy and Switzerland, the United States, Canada, the Dutch East

Indies and Spitsbergen have all yielded good remains. Like their very distant relations the Nothosaurs and Placodonts, they had also divided into two groups of fairly similar habits. A small and not very well-known family of Ichthyosaurs called the Omphalosauridae, represented typically by *Omphalosaurus*, from the Middle Triassic of Nevada, had a short and strong skull, in contrast to the long and rather delicate skull of the typical Ichthyosaurs. The jaws had several rows of small, domed teeth in sockets. These teeth, like

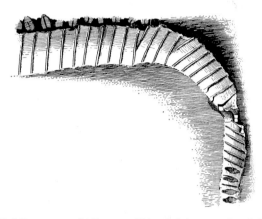

Fig. 38.—Tail fin support of *Mixosaurus*, Trias, Spitsbergen. One-half natural size.

those of the Placodonts, must have been for crushing molluscs, and the family probably represents a shore paddling stage of the evolutionary line. Like the Placodont stage of the Plesiosaurs it did not survive the Triassic.

The other Triassic branch is quite different in character and outcome. The typical representative is *Mixosaurus** ("the mixed lizard"), known from the Middle Trias of Spitsbergen, Switzerland and North Italy and perhaps from Timor in the East Indies. *Mixosaurus* was a fish-shaped swimming reptile from 3 feet up to 7 feet long. The skull was pointed and superficially like that of a dolphin, though in structure it was very different. The neck was short; the front swimming paddles were larger than the hind. The tail was as long as the body and only slightly bent down at the tip with a very small dorsal fin (Fig. 38).

In other words, to all appearances *Mixosaurus* was an Ichthyosaur with a less well-developed tail. There were differences in the

PLATE 9

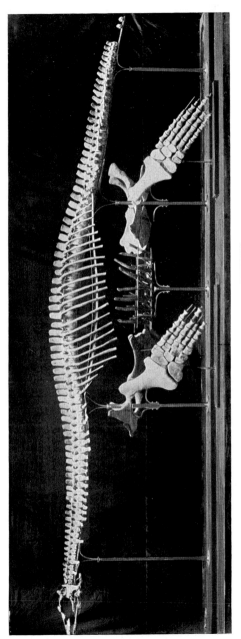

CRYPTOCLEIDUS OXONIENSIS

skeleton, particularly in the jaws, where the teeth were inserted in sockets and not in a continuous groove as in the true Ichthyosaurs. It is clear that the Mixosaurs were a stage on the evolutionary route of the Ichthyosaurs. The latter were well developed and differentiated into many species by Lower Liassic times.

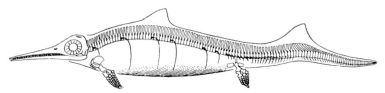

Fig. 39.—Reconstruction of a primitive Ichthyosaur, showing beginning of tail fin development.

Ichthyosaur bones have long been known. Dr. Scheuchzer collected vertebrae in 1705, but thought them to be human bones and evidence of the Flood. One well known associated skeleton of *Ichthyosaurus* was discovered at Lyme Regis by Mary Anning in 1811 when she was twelve; already an assiduous collector of fossils, she hired men to help her to disengage and remove the Ichthyosaur from the stratum in which it lay. Unfortunately the present location of this skeleton is unknown.

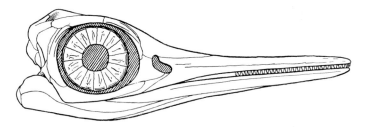

Fig. 40.—Skull of an Ichthyosaur from right side, showing orbit with sclerotic plates, nostril opening in front of eye, and rostrum with sharply pointed teeth.

Ichthyosaurs* were shaped like a large fish or like the modern porpoise. The comparison with the latter is more apt, although the porpoise is a mammal, for the Ichthyosaur was essentially a surface swimmer, breathing by lungs, and with a smooth brownish body, devoid of scales. The skull (Fig. 40) was long and pointed, so that the brain region was comparatively small and the snout large, the mouth being edged along the jaws by very numerous striated conical teeth set in a groove and not in separate sockets (Fig. 42). The jaws and teeth, even more than those of the Plesiosaurs, must have formed a very effective fish-trap.

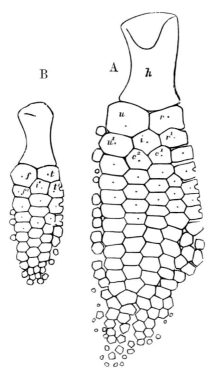

Fig. 41.—Right fore (A) and hind (B) paddles of *Ichthyosaurus* (*Eurypterygius*) *intermedius*, Lower Lias of Lyme Regis; one-third natural size. h, humerus; u, ulna; r, radius; u¹, ulnare; i, intermedium; r¹, radiale; c¹, c², centralia; f, fibula; t, tibia; f¹, fibulare; t¹, tibiale. [After Lydekker.]

The neck was short and the body long, tapering to a large terminal fin like the tail fin of a fish, but this fin is supported by the downward bent vertebral column, in contrast to the upward bend in those fishes with heterocercal tails. In length the animals varied from only a foot up to 30 feet or more. The limbs are unlike those of the Plesiosaurs in both structure and use. The upper limb bones (humerus and femur) are short and stout; the lower bones (radius and ulna, tibia and fibula) are shorter and ovoid, being broader

71

F

than long. The paddle is composed of five or less rows of digits (Fig. 41), represented by small pentagonal or hexagonal pieces of bone which, together with one or more accessory rows in some cases, form a bony mosaic which was stiffened by cartilage and covered with skin. The modern classification of Ichthyosauria is based on the relationship of the intermedium of the carpus or wrist joint and one or two digits. The genus *Ichthyosaurus** (*Eurypterygius*) and others in which the intermedium bears two digits are known as latipinnate; others, in which only one digit is borne, as longipinnate (*Stenopterygius** and *Leptopterygius**). In both groups, the front paddles are larger than the hind, sometimes markedly so. It is clear that the propulsion of the animal was accomplished through the movements of the tail fin, and the paddles served as keels to maintain balance and to change direction. Whereas there is ample skeletal evidence for the tail fin and the paddles, impressions of the skin show that there was also a triangular dorsal fin, without any bony support at all, midway between the paddles (Plate 11).

Specimens are known in good condition from England, but some of the German examples from the Upper Lias are remarkable and reveal very many details of the structure and appearance. One of these specimens, with an outline of the body preserved, is shown under a movable blind in the Fossil Reptile Gallery.

For many years it has been observed that some of these specimens contain the remains of small individuals either within the body cavity or adjacent to it. Where it has been possible to identify the small skeletons they have proved to be identical with the larger individual. There can be little doubt that they are remains of unborn young. Many reptiles have the eggs developed within the mother's body and the young born alive, that is, they are ovo-viviparous. This would be an enormous advantage to the Ichthyosaurs, for they would then be no longer dependent upon the shore but would have the freedom of the seas. Certainly, their remains suggest this widespread range for, from the Lower Lias to the upper part of the Cretaceous, they have been found in almost every part of the world. The most representative and most numerous collection is in this Museum.

The bony remains are very often picked up by collectors. Pieces of the rostrum or snout with teeth are not uncommon. The teeth themselves are long and fluted, slightly curved and with a sharp point. The whole tooth has a comparatively massive base (Fig. 42)

PLATE 10

and the ornamentation is restricted to the upper part. The vertebrae, being numerous, are fairly frequently found. They are always free

Fig. 42.—Ichthyosaurian tooth. The cavity at the base was for the developing germ tooth. One-half natural size.

of the neural arch elements and are therefore discs, thin as compared with their height and breadth, and are hollowed on each face, so that in section they have an hour-glass shape (Fig. 43). Usually

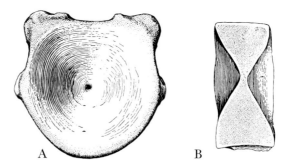

Fig. 43.—Ichthyosaurian vertebra. A, anterior view; B, sectional view. One-half natural size.

rounded, they are in some species subtriangular. The hinder part of the skull is not so commonly found, largely because it is delicately built, but some of the Museum specimens show it well. The orbit

74

PLATE 11

OPHTHALMOSAURUS

is large and contains in many cases evidences of the bony ring of sclerotic plates that once supported the eye. In one genus, *Ophthalmosaurus*,* of which a complete specimen is exhibited, the eye is relatively enormous, and the genus is additionally interesting because it was almost toothless. Its paddles are broad for their size and were probably rather flexible because of the cartilage that surrounded the constituent bones. *Ophthalmosaurus* comes from the Oxford Clay, especially of Peterborough (Plate 11).

Many Ichthyosaurs are found in later deposits up to the Chalk, but then grow rarer, and they appear to have become extinct in the later stages of the Cretaceous, leaving their companions the Plesiosaurs and the great Mosasaurs temporarily in possession of the seas.

X. CROCODILES

The crocodiles (Order Crocodilia) have a long history and were widely distributed in the Mesozoic, but they show little change in essentials throughout their range. Their origin is of considerable importance, not only for its own interest but also for the relationship revealed with certain other great groups which have yet to be mentioned.

During the earlier part of the Mesozoic there was an Order of reptiles distributed over the lands and in the shallow waters known as the Thecodontia. They were generally small animals, a few feet long at most, and nearly all of them had a dermal armour developed to some extent. The character from which they derive their name is that their teeth are implanted in deep sockets, each tooth being hollow with its successor developing in that hollow base. Many of the Thecodonts were terrestrial and were, or showed a tendency to become, bipedal. Such were the Pseudosuchia, which will be referred to again in connexion with the Dinosaurs. On the other hand, there were Thecodonts with large pointed skulls, sometimes 3 feet long, and with teeth suited for a fleshy diet. These animals, known generally as the Phytosauria, were aquatic and their remains bear very close superficial resemblances to the crocodiles.

*Belodon** (Fig. 44) is one of these. In it the skull is very much like that of a long-snouted crocodile, though it is rather high-crested in profile, and the dorsal scutes on the body increase the general similarity. The shoulder and pelvic girdles are, however, much more primitive, and, as a relic of the bipedality of the Order, the Phytosaurs have the hind limbs longer than the front. *Belodon* itself comes from the Upper Trias of Germany; *Mystriosuchus*,* rather less robust, is also from the Upper Trias of southern Germany. Other genera come from the Upper Trias of various parts of the United States.

On grounds of appearance and habits as well as of geological age, it used to be considered that the Phytosaurs were ancestral crocodiles. That view is no longer held, and it is now clear that the Phytosaurs were merely precursors, supplanted during the early Jurassic by true crocodiles, which proved to be better adapted in the same habitat.

The ancestry of the crocodiles must be sought elsewhere, and within recent years work that has been done in the American Museum of Natural History upon their collections from Arizona has done much to point the way. From the Dinosaur Canyon beds (Triassic) there have come the remains of a remarkable primitive

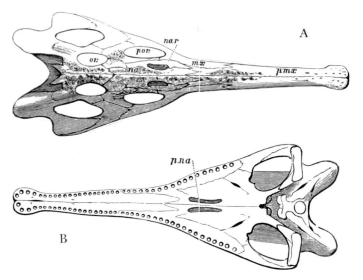

Fig. 44.—Skull of *Belodon kapffi*, upper (A) and palatal (B) views, from the Keuper of Württemberg; about one-eighth natural size. pmx, premaxilla; mx, maxilla; na, nasal; nar, external narial opening; or, orbit; p.na, posterior nares; p.or, preorbital vacuity. [After H. von Meyer.]

crocodilian known as *Protosuchus richardsoni*. A careful and detailed examination of the structure of this animal, which has been fairly fully recovered, shows that it is a crocodile and not a Phytosaur. It is a small creature, about 3 feet in length. The skull is also small and rather flat, the snout being short, and there are a few specialized but un-crocodilian characters. None the less, the shoulder and pelvic girdles and the limbs are all typically crocodilian in plan and arrangement. The body armour is heavy.

Protosuchus strongly resembles two genera, *Erythrochampsa* and *Notochampsa* from the Upper Stormberg (Triassic) beds of South Africa. Together they represent a sub-order, the Protosuchia, of ancient and primitive crocodiles. Unfortunately, none of these genera is represented in the Museum collection.

The Jurassic and Lower Cretaceous crocodiles are known as the Mesosuchia. They are characterized by flattened, slightly cupped articular ends of the vertebrae. They never have the ball-and-socket kind of articulation of the living crocodiles (Figs. 49, 50). Nor have any of the Mesosuchia a complete bony palate. It is true that there was a certain amount of backward growth of the palatines and maxillae, but unless this was continued by some fleshy structure the secondary palate would not be complete and the animal would

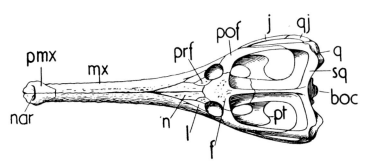

Fig. 45.—*Steneosaurus durobrivensis*, upper aspect of skull. Oxford Clay of Peterborough. nar, narial opening; pmx, premaxilla; mx, maxilla; n, nasal; l, lachrymal; prf, prefrontal; f, frontal; pof, postfrontal; pt, pterygoid; par, parietal; j, jugal; qj, quadrato-jugal; q, quadrate; sq, squamosal; boc, basioccipital. About one-twelfth natural size.

not be able to open its mouth under water and simultaneously breathe through the nostrils for any length of time, as is essential for modern crocodiles when drowning their prey.

The early Mesosuchia were all marine. They were well armoured by a paired series of broad plates above and a mosaic of smaller polygonal plates below. Typical genera are *Steneosaurus** (Fig. 45), *Teleosaurus,** *Pelagosaurus** (Fig. 46) and *Mystriosaurus.**

Steneosaurus was long and slender with a skull about 3 feet long. Excellent specimens, collected by A. N. Leeds in the Oxford Clay of Peterborough, are exhibited. The dorsal plates of this genus are connected by a peg-and-socket joint. In *Teleosaurus* the jaws are long, slender and straight-edged, and the teeth are directed outwards, so that the upper and lower series more or less interlock. The museum has a valuable collection from the Lower Jurassic of England and of Normandy. *Pelagosaurus,** similar to *Teleosaurus* except for some characters in the skull, is seldom more than 6 feet in total length; it has been found in several Upper Liassic localities in England, France and Germany.

Mystriosaurus* differs in having the tip of the snout expanded and the teeth arranged vertically in the jaws. It is an important member of the group because so many of its anatomical features have been preserved in specimens from the Upper Lias of Holzmaden in

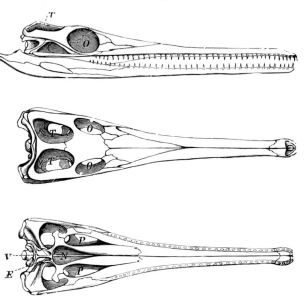

Fig. 46.—Skull of *Pelagosaurus typus*, Upper Lias of Normandy; one-quarter natural size. Right side view, upper view and palate. E, opening of median eustachian canal; N, posterior nares; O, orbits; P, palatine vacuities; T, supratemporal fossae; V, basioccipital bone. [After Owen.]

Germany. In addition to excellent skeletons up to nearly 20 feet long, even the tracheal rings, the impression of the webs between the toes, and stomach contents have been found. Stomach-stones stained black with the ink of cuttle-fish give a clue to the diet of these crocodiles.

Many of the Upper Jurassic genera, such as *Geosaurus** and *Metriorhynchus** (which may be identical), show extreme adaptation for life in the sea. They have the elongated snout characteristic of most aquatic animals, and they have large, laterally compressed teeth in sockets. Whereas all modern crocodiles have strongly sculptured skulls, these are only slightly sculptured or even quite smooth. Since the end of the backbone turns down slightly the tail must have borne a small terminal fin, similar to but smaller than that of the Ichthyosaurs. The fore limbs are small but the hinder are large and must have been used in swimming. There are no bony plates on the body, so that the skin must have been as smooth as that of the Ichthyosaurs or the modern porpoises. A

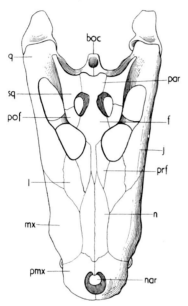

Fig. 47.—*Diplocynodon hantoniensis*, Tertiary of England. Upper aspect of skull. Abbreviations as in Fig. 45. About one-third natural size.

remarkably fine skeleton of *Geosaurus*, from the famous Lithographic Stone of Eichstätt, Bavaria, shows the outline of the body and tail fin.

During the Cretaceous there were many crocodiles which in appearance and habits approached those living today. *Goniopholis,** from the Upper Jurassic and Lower Cretaceous of Europe and North America, is most typical of the Wealden and Purbeck beds and many splendid specimens have been obtained from English deposits. The stout skull, rounded with a moderately long snout, is of the modern crocodilian shape and not of the gavial type. The Wealden species, *Goniopholis crassidens*, has a skull nearly 2 feet long, but the Purbeck species, *G. simus*, is smaller, and is only about 7 feet in total length. There is no doubt that these were marsh-living crocodiles with strong and muscular jaws adapted to seizing a prey of some considerable size. Among contemporary dwarf forms from the Purbeck of Swanage *Nannosuchus** may be described as a miniature *Goniopholis*, with a skull length that never exceeded 5 inches; *Theriosuchus** was much more like the modern true crocodiles in appearance but was less than 2 feet in total length. These

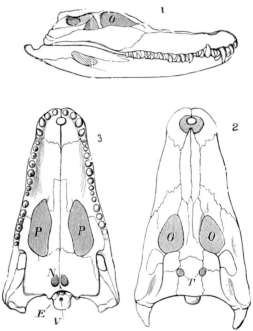

Fig. 48.—Skull of *Crocodylus palustris*, a living Indian form. 1. Right side view; 2. Upper view; 3. Palate. About one-eighth natural size. E, opening of median eustachian canal; N, posterior nares; O, orbits; P, palatopterygoid vacuities; T, supratemporal fossae; V, basioccipital bone.

appear to have been adapted for the capture of the small and presumably succulent warm-blooded mammals whose remains have been discovered in the same deposits. At the other end of the scale is *Phobosuchus hatcheri*, from the Upper Cretaceous of America, which is thought to have preyed on the great dinosaurs. A reconstructed cast of the complete skull is exhibited; this suggests that the whole animal must have been about 45 feet long.

By the Upper Cretaceous and the Tertiary periods the crocodiles were to all intents and purposes of kinds with which we are now familiar, although their geographical distribution is different. By Cretaceous times, the ball-and-socket joint between the vertebrae had been introduced and the secondary palate was fully formed. Tomistomids, like the living *Tomistoma* of the East Indies, are represented in the Eocene of England and Belgium by *Dollosuchus dixoni*, and the genus *Thoracosaurus* is much more widely spread.

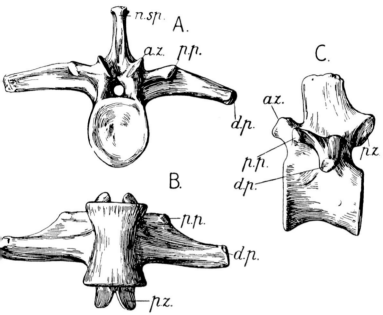

Fig. 49.—Dorsal vertebra of *Metriorhynchus moreli*. Oxford Clay of Peterborough. A, from front; B, from below; C, from left side. One-half natural size. a.z. anterior zygapophysis; d.p, diapophysial process; n.sp, neural spine; p.p, parapophysial process; p.z, posterior zygapophysis. [From Andrews.]

The alligators, abundant in the Lower Tertiary of Europe, include *Diplocynodon** (Fig. 47). True crocodiles such as *Phobosuchus** and *Crocodylus** itself (Fig. 48) appear in the Upper Cretaceous. The gavials are represented by part of the jaw of *Rhamphosuchus** from the Pliocene of the Siwalik Hills, India. This creature must have been about 50 feet in length and thus is the largest known crocodilian.

The cooling of the climate in the temperate zone has reduced the range and speciation of crocodiles at the present time.

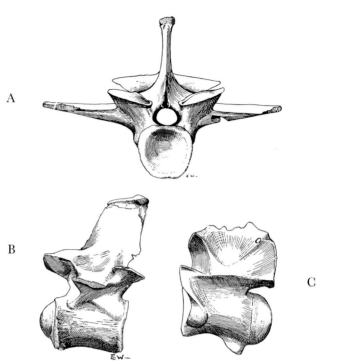

Fig. 50.—Vertebrae of *Diplocynodon hantoniensis*. A, B, dorsal vertebrae, from front and from right side respectively. C, cervical vertebra, from left side. A, B, one-half natural size; C, one and a half natural size. Processes as in Fig. 49.

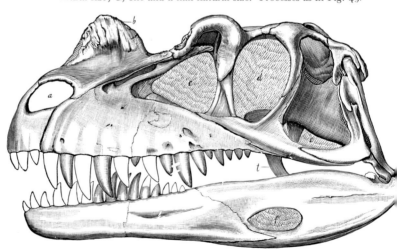

Fig. 51.—Skull and mandible of *Ceratosaurus nasicornis*, left side view, from the Upper Jurassic of Colorado; one-sixth natural size. a, nostril; b, horn core; c, preorbital vacuity; d, orbit; e, lateral temporal fossa; f, vacuity in mandible; t, transverse bone. [After Marsh.]

XI. DINOSAURS—SAURISCHIA

One of the best-known groups of fossil reptiles, and certainly the most popular, is that of the Dinosaurs. The vast size or strange form of many of these no doubt explains this attraction, but the group exhibits various points of anatomical and physiological interest, and has many important evolutionary lessons for the student.

The name Dinosauria was given to three genera in 1842 by Richard Owen (afterwards the first Director of the Natural History Museum). These, with another that Owen then regarded as a crocodile (*Cetiosaurus*), represent the four lesser divisions into which the group is now sometimes divided.

Most of the land-reptiles of the Jurassic and Cretaceous periods and some of their predecessors of the Trias are popularly referred to as Dinosaurs. The group is not a natural one, for the two chief and distinct sections of it contain reptiles of different origin which display persistent differences in important skeletal features. All are, however, nearly related to the crocodiles; but all have well-formed limb bones, almost invariably adapted for the habitual support of the animal on land.

Some of them were massive animals that must have walked on all fours, and are shown by their teeth to have been plant-eaters. Others walked only on the hind legs, and while some of these bipeds were herbivorous, others with sabre-like cutting teeth were carnivorous. The large and often laterally compressed tail of some of the bipeds suggests that they were amphibious.

The two great groups, Saurischia and Ornithischia, which comprise the Dinosaurs have separate lines of descent, but both derive undoubtedly from the Thecodontia which in the later stages of the Trias gave birth to the ancestors of the Dinosaurs, Pterodactyls, Crocodiles and the Birds.

The first constituent group is called the Saurischi because the disposition of the bones of the pelvis is on the usual reptilian plan and is therefore triradiate. Other characters are the situation and direction of the bones, especially the quadrate, that articulate the lower jaw with the skull (Fig. 51). Saurischia almost always have teeth in front of the mouth and quite often also have the series continued towards the hinder part of the jaws (cf. p. 85).

85

The Saurischia are themselves divisible into two sub-orders—the bipedal carnivores classed together as the Theropoda; and large, sometimes gigantic, browsing quadrupeds known collectively as the Sauropoda.

THEROPODA

The Theropoda ("beast-feet") comprise the carnivorous dinosaurs with, in many cases, a lightly built skull and skeleton, though others were heavy and formidable. The teeth were like little sabres and set in sockets along the jaws (Fig. 51). The fore limbs were always shorter than the hind and both fingers and toes had prehensile claws. This difference in size of limbs is reminiscent of the ancestral thecodont condition, and suggests that, as a rule, the fore limbs were not used in walking or running. To maintain the balance of the body in movement the strong and muscular tail must have been stretched out behind and off the ground. The hip girdle, of course, is characteristically triradiate and rather like that of the crocodiles (Fig. 52, A).

The remains of Theropod dinosaurs have been found in Mesozoic rocks in many parts of the world. They are well known in Europe and North America and have also been discovered in South America, North, East and South Africa, India, U.S.S.R., China and Mongolia. The Triassic forms of both Europe and North America are either small and lightly built or large and cumbrous, and both kinds had a place in the subsequent development of the group. The former are represented in the Museum by *Saltopus* from the Triassic Sandstone of Moray in Scotland, and perhaps by the less known *Thecodontosaurus* from the Triassic of the Bristol district. American representatives of this lightly built type are much better known, making it clear that from such dinosaurs the large predators of the Jurassic and the Cretaceous were derived.

Most of the remains of Theropoda from the English Jurassic and Wealden beds are referred to *Megalosaurus*,* though, with the exception of one skeleton, the genus is not well known and includes much scattered and fragmentary material. This is, however, all of importance, certainly historically, and the first dinosaur specimens ever to be described scientifically were the fragments of the jaw which Dr. Buckland of Oxford dealt with in 1824. This material came from the Stonesfield Slate. *Megalosaurus* is also known from northern France. In contrast to the general state of incompleteness

PLATE 12

MEGALOSAURUS

G

that characterizes most representatives of the genus is the fine skeleton in the University Museum, Oxford, known as *Megalosaurus* (*Eustreptospondylus*) *cuvieri* (Plate 12). The British Museum contains a fine skull of a Megalosaur with a horned nose, described by A. S. Woodward as *Megalosaurus bradleyi*.* The Megalosaurs were certainly predators of some power, running on the strong hind limbs, with the shorter front limbs used only in resting and feeding. The head and shoulders would almost inevitably be carried in a rather stooping position (see Plate 12), and not in the upright pose adopted in most restorations.

The Megalosaurs varied from 10 to 30 feet in total length, as measured from the snout along the backbone to the tip of the tail. The skull was at least a foot long, with a lower jaw that could open widely. The teeth were sharp, laterally compressed and with serrated edges. Many of them became recurved as they grew. They were thus aggressive weapons of considerable effectiveness. The fore limbs were markedly shorter than the hind and were obviously not used for progression; the hands had five clawed fingers. The hind legs, however, were strong and muscular. The hind feet had three functional toes, each with a sharp claw. The tail was moderately long and somewhat flattened from side to side.

One can visualize them as animals of prey of some physical ability, though their mental alertness was very much less than that of a mammal. Savage attacks on a living prey were possible, but the Megalosaurs were possibly carrion feeders as well. That they were always active pursuers is most unlikely, for whatever their appearance in pictures may suggest they were still reptiles, compelled by their physiological make-up to have short bursts of activity, with its inevitable increase in body temperature, followed by longish spells of rest and cooling off. This is a factor that must never be forgotten with regard to the dinosaurs, for the many fanciful restorations often suggest an activity far above the reptilian level. In reptiles the body temperature varies according to that of the external temperature, and the amount of heat generated on activity is developed as the cube of the body-weight, whereas the cooling to ordinary temperature levels is in accordance with the square of the surface; hence there might be an unavoidable lag between heat developed and heat lost that demands time for the establishment of an equilibrium. It is equally unlikely for purely anatomical reasons that these predators leapt upon their prey for the kill, though they are sometimes shown in this way in restorations.

Ceratosaurus, one of the typical American forms, was about 17 feet long measured over the backbone. The skull was nearly 20 inches long and furnished with sharp teeth (Fig. 51). The neck was comparatively short and the body and tail long. The hind limbs were markedly longer and more muscular than the fore limbs and it is significant that the metatarsals of the feet were fused into a firm and compact structure, for this indicates an efficient and somewhat advanced foot mechanism. The hand, however, was five-fingered. *Ceratosaurus* is unique among Theropods in having small bony ossicles on its back, It comes from the famous Morrison Formation of Colorado, that has produced so many fine specimens. Among them is another well-known carnivorous dinosaur, *Antrodemus* [*Allosaurus*], which was larger and more muscular than *Ceratosaurus*. Indeed, an average *Antrodemus* was 35 feet when measured along the backbone and the skull was nearly 30 inches long. The teeth were strong, serrated, recurved and admirably suited for tearing to pieces the smaller dinosaurs. *Antrodemus* was also furnished with claws that were equally terrible.

The largest forms are known as Dinodonts. They are best known from America in *Albertosaurus* (*Gorgosaurus*) and *Tyrannosaurus* The latter is the most specialized and the largest of them all of any age. *Tarbosaurus*,* a somewhat similar form, comes from Mongolia.

*Tyrannosaurus** was large in head and in body. Its total length might have been nearly 50 feet, of which the skull took up 4 feet. The gait was, as usual, bipedal; the jaws, which could be opened very widely, had sharp teeth 4–5 inches long and the head would normally be carried some 16 feet off the ground. The hind limbs were very powerful and ended in feet with three functional toes, though the small first digit was still present. The ridiculously small fore limbs had two fingers only which, even though they were clawed, can only have had some specialized use and could not perhaps reach the mouth.

Even if there is no obvious connexion between the large carnivores and their Triassic predecessors, it is easy to see where some sort of the latter led. In the later Cretaceous there were small dinosaurs which seem to have been adapted for a different kind of life from that of the Albertosaurs and Tyrannosaurs. Such was *Ornithomimus* a bipedal dinosaur about 13 feet in total length. The hind limbs were comparatively long, but the fore limbs were also long and slender and there were five long tapering fingers in the hands, suggesting they were used actively. The neck was long and must have been somewhat like that of an ostrich: the tail, too, was long and slender. The skull was small and light and was set at right angles to the neck, thus conforming to the position of the ostrich head. In some specimens the delicate skull with large orbits still has the fine sclerotic plates preserved. The jaws are toothless. We thus have a typically carnivorous kind of dinosaur so far as its skeleton is concerned, which must have become herbivorous. Presumably the animal lived on fruits or soft vegetable substances which might be plucked off by the hands and which it could masticate without teeth. The remains of these kinds of dinosaurs are known only from North America and Asia.

During the Trias there was a large predacious dinosaur known as *Plateosaurus** whose development must be discussed briefly. Its remains have been found in such numbers in South Germany as to suggest that the animals lived in small herds. *Plateosaurus* was heavily and awkwardly built. The head was small but the body was large, and the limbs showed little disparity in size and development. The structure of the shoulder girdle suggests that both hind and fore limbs could be used in walking for short periods, but the bipedal pose would be generally adopted. The whole animal, when fully grown, would be about 20 feet long and with its powerful teeth and sharp claws must have been a formidable adversary.

It has been suggested that the climate of the time was continental, with two marked seasons, one moist and one rather dry. The geological circumstances of the occurrence of this dinosaur's remains suggest that during the moist time of year *Plateosaurus* occupied more hilly country with coniferous vegetation and presumably therefore with a good supply of herbivorous reptiles on which to prey. During the dry season the Plateosaurs were attracted to the waters of the deltas and lakes in the region, where no doubt they found fish and reptiles in plenty.

Several details of the anatomical structure and the teeth of *Plateosaurus* suggest a resemblance to other large dinosaurs that were to become widely distributed during the later stages of the Mesozoic. It is certain that *Plateosaurus* itself is not the ancestor of these reptiles, but some related form living more or less constantly by the shores of a lake may in course of time have been attracted, or compelled, to adopt a more amphibious role and thus to become the first of a great sub-order, the Sauropoda.

SAUROPODA

The Sauropods are among the most fantastic of all reptiles and some were the largest land animals we know. A typical Sauropod had a small skull, a long and relatively thin neck, an elephantine body and a long, thin, tapering tail. The largest of them were animals of very great bulk, probably weighing 80 tons or so. *Diplodocus*, which had the longest skeleton, though it was not the bulkiest animal, was 85 feet long. It is quite natural, therefore, that there should be general interest in the mechanics and habits of animals like these. They were obviously highly specialized, yet they were world-wide in distribution, and lasted throughout the Jurassic and, in some parts of the world, on into the later stages of the Cretaceous.

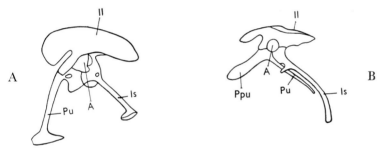

Fig. 52.—Saurischian pelvis (A) and Ornithischian pelvis (B) from left side. *A*, acetabulum; *Il*, ilium; *Is*, ischium; *Pu*, pubis; *Ppu*, prepubis.

The earliest Sauropods are found in the Jurassic, but they probably arose from a *Plateosaurus*-like Prosauropod of the Trias. Traces of their bipedal ancestry linger in the skeleton. They have the same kind of pelvic arrangement as their Theropod relatives; and though all Sauropods walked on all fours, this pose was of secondary adoption, and most of them still show the fore limb rather shorter than the hind. Most of them had five-fingered hands and five-toed feet and, since digits are not likely to have been acquired, the Sauropods must be descended from a bipedal ancestor which had five digits in both also. It is this primitive condition that gives them their name of "reptile-feet".

Their teeth are arranged on the usual Theropod plan, and always developed in the front of the jaws; where reduction takes place, it is at the hinder end of the series. The teeth differ in shape and character from those of the Theropods in being generally rather spoon-shaped or spatulate (Fig. 54). From this it may be argued that they were used for a herbivorous diet.

Fig. 53.—Tooth of *Thecodontosaurus platyodon*, Upper Trias of Bristol; natural size.

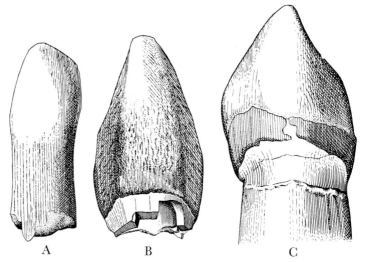

Fig. 54.—Teeth of English Sauropod Dinosaurs. A, *Pleurocoelus valdensis*; B, *Hoplosaurus armatus*; C, *Cetiosaurus leedsi*. All natural size.

The Sauropod skeleton shows marked contrasts within itself. Compared with the bulk of the animal much of the backbone shows a remarkable combination of lightness and strength, the excavation and buttressing of some of the vertebrae being of high engineering economy and efficiency. This can best be seen on the neck and trunk vertebrae. It is not observed on tail vertebrae and is in striking contrast to the solid and heavy bones of the limbs. It has been pointed out by many authors that the distribution of the

PLATE 13

CETIOSAURUS

light and the weighty parts is above and below a line joining the
upper parts of the shoulder and pelvic girdles. These girdles were
strong and well developed for the attachment of the powerful
muscles for the limbs. The heavy feet were plantigrade and padded,
with some of the fingers and toes bearing large and strong claws.
It would seem clear from the size and weight of the Sauropods that
such claws were not for seizing prey.

The skeletal details suggest that Sauropods were much too heavy
for continual activity on the land, and it seems most probable that
they lived in the shoreward waters of lakes and estuaries. Here
they probably browsed upon aquatic and shore vegetation, though
from time to time the females would be compelled to lay their eggs
upon the shore. Remains of eggs attributed to the Sauropods are
known from Europe and Africa and so far there has been no discovery suggesting that in any form the eggs were hatched within the
body of the mother.

The distribution of lightness and weight in the skeleton is con-
sistent with an aquatic habitat. The nature and distribution of
the teeth in the jaws would seem to confirm it, and the discovery
of footprints clearly outlined in the former bottom of a shallow river
helps to complete the picture. A restoration of *Cetiosaurus** is shown
in Plate 13.

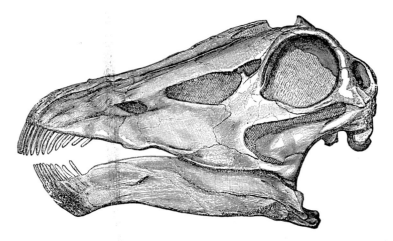

Fig. 55.—Skull and mandible of *Diplodocus*, left side view, Upper Jurassic of
Colorado. One-sixth natural size. The large round vacuity is the orbit and the
cleft immediately above it is the nostril. [After Marsh.]

A plaster cast of the skeleton of *Diplodocus carnegii** is a well-known and popular exhibit, largely on account of its impressive size, and it shows admirably the main characters of the group as outlined above. A notable feature of the skull (Fig. 55) is that the nostril is situated on top of the head. This is characteristic only of the families Diplodocidae and perhaps the Titanosauridae. In all other forms the nostril is on the face but below the level of the eyes. This, of course, suggests that in the case of *Diplodocus*, so long as the upper half of the head was above water, the animal could pull in vegetation with the rake-like teeth and could see and breathe comfortably above the level of the water.

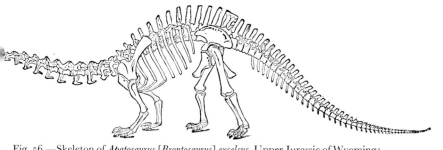

Fig. 56.—Skeleton of *Apatosaurus* [*Brontosaurus*] *excelsus*, Upper Jurassic of Wyoming; about 1/150th natural size. [After Marsh.]

There is every reason to believe that these animals spent much of their time with their necks along the surface of the water or just awash. This would render them almost invisible and at the same time solve the real mechanical problems involved in some of the poses attributed to them in many restoration pictures.

The brain of these animals can be partly reconstructed and evaluated from casts taken from the brain cavity. In *Diplodocus* it was small, no larger than a hen's egg, and it was not highly organized. There can have been little intelligence in these Dinosaurs.

The *Diplodocus* exhibited is a cast of a composite skeleton made from three individuals from the Jurassic of Utah and Colorado, and was presented in 1910 by Andrew Carnegie. The gallery also contains original bones including the partial skeleton of *Ceticsaurus leedsi*, from the Oxford Clay of Peterborough, discovered by Alfred N. Leeds, in 1898, which must have belonged to a reptile nearly 60 feet in total length. Detached bones from the same specimen are also on view and show evidence of damage or disease.

Some of the bones in the Dinosaur Gallery, such as the humerus of *Brachiosaurus,** which is 7 feet 1 inch long, suggest enormous sizes for some of these Sauropods, but whereas some, such as *Diplodocus,* were long and comparatively low in stature, others like *Brachiosaurus* were high at the shoulder but not excessively long in the body. The two kinds lived more or less contemporaneously and most of them died out early in the Cretaceous. However, the Titanosauridae lingered on almost to the close of the Cretaceous.

It is not difficult to suggest reasons for their general extinction. Their restricted habitat, their cumbrousness and low intelligence were no great hindrances in settled conditions, but general and local geographical changes recurrent in the Mesozoic would compel them either to leave a region or to remain and die. Since they must have been physically incapable of extensive migration whole groups of them must have suffered local extinction throughout the Jurassic and early Cretaceous.

Climate may also have been a powerful factor in determining their disappearance or survival, as the persistence of some kinds in the warmer lands during later Cretaceous times suggests.

PLATE 14

HYPSILOPHODON

XII. DINOSAURS—ORNITHISCHIA

The second major group of the dinosaurs also contains bipedal and quadrupedal members, and although many of them were comparatively large animals none reached a size approaching that of the Sauropods. The bipedal members were unarmoured, the quadrupedal were armoured in one way or another; all were herbivorous.

There are so few indications of Ornithischians in the Trias that doubts had been expressed about the evolutionary connexions between this group and the Thecodonts, but it seems highly probable that they are derived from the same Pseudosuchian stock that earlier gave origin to the carnivorous dinosaurs.

The most obvious characters in the skeleton that differentiate the Ornithischia from the Saurischia are the structure of the pelvis; the direction of the quadrate and the relative position of the jaw articulation; and an additional element at the front end of the lower jaw.

Whereas the Saurischia, as we have seen, have the more typical reptilian triradiate arrangement of the ilium, ischium and pubis, the Ornithischians, whether bipedal or quadrupedal, have a quadriradiate structure. The upper end of the pubis is forked and obliquely T-shaped, with a broader anterior portion which acts as a partial support to the belly, and a more or less pointed posterior portion which makes a comparatively small angle with the shaft of the pubis, which appears to have been turned around, and has come to lie close to the shaft of the ischium in direction and length (Fig. 52, B). This arrangement, which produces a long and strong base for muscular attachment in the bipedal forms, was undoubtedly brought about by the connexions necessary between the pelvic appendages and the tail. The Ornithischia were never so upright as the carnivorous dinosaurs, and the whole balance, and the resting position on the ground, were different.

In the skull the quadrate was either vertical or directed downwards and forwards so that the articulation of the jaws was never at the very back of the skull and was usually some way in front of the occipital condyle. This means that the gape was not so wide as in the carnivores and that there was a more stable position for the slight rotational movements of the jaws in chewing vegetation. Cheek pouches were very probably developed in many forms.

ORNITHOPODA

Only a few primitive Ornithischians, such as the English *Hypsilophodon*, have teeth all along the premaxillae. Usually this region is edentulous, a horny beak being developed on it and in opposition to this a new jaw element, the predentary, appears in the anterior portion of the lower jaw.

The teeth usually have fluted and expanded crowns, though in some Ornithischians a number of teeth may be compressed together into a mosaic.

The earliest definite Ornithischian comes from the Red Beds (Upper Trias) of South Africa. It was found in 1924 and was named *Lycorhinus*.* It has affinities with both *Hypsilophodon* and *Iguanodon*. The best known of the stratigraphically earlier Ornithischia is *Camptosaurus*,* from both England and the United States. It is typical of the bipedal forms, known collectively as Ornithopoda ("bird feet"). It is not, however, the most primitive, for *Hypsilophodon* from the Wealden of England, and *Thescelosaurus* from the Upper Cretaceous of Canada and the United States, have premaxillae bearing teeth, as have *Lycorhinus* and *Fabrosaurus*.

In *Hypsilophodon** the hand was five-fingered, the fifth finger being small and at right angles to the wrist. The foot still had four functional toes, the fifth being vestigial. A fully grown specimen was about 4 or 5 feet long as measured over the backbone and tail, but, when walking, the head was only just over 2 feet from the ground. Although the length of the fingers and toes of *Hypsilophodon* appear to suggest arboreal abilities for the dinosaur the presence of two rows of small bony plates along the centre of the back do not support the contention. These are, however, of great interest, for they show, thus early in the Ornithischian story, the development of features that must long have been latent in the stock. The Thecodonts, as was pointed out, had this propensity, and the armoured relatives of *Hypsilophodon*, however distant that relationship might be, showed the development of this bony potentiality to the full. This may, however, be a matter of little real significance and certainly so far as we know *Hypsilophodon* was not the ancestor of any armoured or otherwise more advanced form.

A near relative of *Hypsilophodon*, which shows some of its features on an enlarged scale, is *Iguanodon* (Plates 15, 16), also well represented in beds of Wealden age. Historically, *Iguanodon* is of great importance, for it is the earliest known dinosaur of which we have well authenticated remains. In 1822, a worn and unspectacular remnant of a tooth (Fig. 57) was found on the roadside by the wife of the famous geologist and physician, Gideon Mantell. Mantell was struck by the appearance of the tooth and realized with much perspicacity that it belonged to a hitherto unknown animal. After careful study he decided that it and those subsequently found closely resembled the teeth of the living Iguana and he therefore named it *Iguanodon* (Iguana-tooth). During the next few years, Mantell

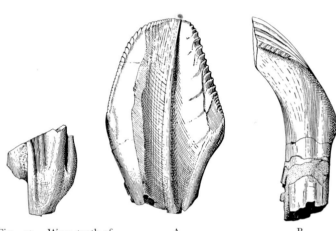

Fig. 57.—Worn tooth of *Iguanodon* discovered by Mrs. Mantell in 1822. Natural size.

A B
Fig. 58.—Teeth of *Iguanodon*. A. inner aspect of a crown from right lower jaw; B, hinder aspect of tooth from left lower jaw. Both natural size.

discovered further specimens of teeth and several bones, though not in an association that led to any real understanding of the size and structure of the animal. In 1834, however, a specimen was discovered in a quarry at Maidstone which showed both bones and the impression of a tooth that proved, once for all, the relationship of the remains.

Subsequent discoveries, especially a remarkable find of nearly thirty skeletons in 1878 at Bernissart, near Mons, in Belgium, revealed most of the details of the animal's osteology and enabled palaeontologists to re-create much of its appearance and habits.

Mantell's original specimens and the Maidstone fossil are in this Museum and have since been named *Iguanodon mantelli;** the Bernissart specimens are all in the Institut Royal des Sciences Naturelles in Brussels, but an excellent cast of one of the most

PLATE 15

IGUANODON

complete specimens is also on exhibition in the Dinosaur Gallery.

*Iguanodon bernissartensis,** as the largest species is named, stands about 16 feet high, though as measured along the backbone the animal is just over 31 feet long. The head is large but rather narrow, having at the front a toothless beak formed by the curved pre-maxilla above and by the predentary below. The comparatively small fore limbs end in a five-fingered hand, in which, however, the thumb was a bony spur. This was originally thought to be a horn on the nose of the animal and appears as such in the earliest restoration. The pelvis is arranged on very much the same plan as is that of an ostrich, but the bones are not fused together and the pubis is relatively larger. The three-toed feet are again arranged very much like those of one of the young running birds before the bones consolidate. The tail, deep and slightly compressed laterally, might have been used in swimming; obviously it played a great part in maintaining balance. Many of the tendons were ossified, especially along the neural spines of the vertebrae.

Most of these features are also well displayed on the almost complete skeleton of a smaller species, *Iguanodon atherfieldensis,** recovered in 1917 from the Isle of Wight (Plate 16). The three-toed footprints of *Iguanodon* are sometimes seen in the Wealden rocks of Sussex. Good examples of them from the Purbeck beds of Dorset are exhibited in the Dinosaur Gallery near the skeletons. Good remains and teeth of *Iguanodon* have recently been discovered in North Africa.

The first dinosaur ever to be recorded from the United States of America is closely related to *Iguanodon*. When discovered in Montana in 1856 the name *Hadrosaurus* was applied to it, hence the family of dinosaurs to which it belongs is called the Hadrosauridae. The best-known member of the family for many reasons has been *Trachodon,** most of whose representatives have now been renamed *Anatosaurus* (the "duck-reptile") because of some uncertainties in the original description. One of the main characters of this group of dinosaurs is that they had bills like those of ducks at the front of the mouth; the family is often called the duck-bill dinosaurs.

*Anatosaurus** was not unlike *Iguanodon* in general characters and in size. It was a biped and a vegetarian, but the skull was different. The hand had only four fingers, the thumb being absent, and the fingers were connected by a web of skin. The foot was still three-toed, like that of *Iguanodon*, but here the toes, with tuberculated

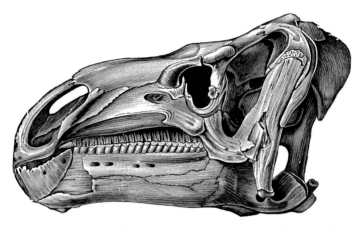

Fig. 59.—Skull and mandible of *Iguanodon bernissartensis*, left side view, Wealden of Belgium; about one-eighth natural size. The toothless predentary bone is shown at the front end of the lower jaw; above it is the oval nostril; the eye is above the end of the tooth row, and the deep and narrow lateral temporal fossa is behind. [After Dollo.]

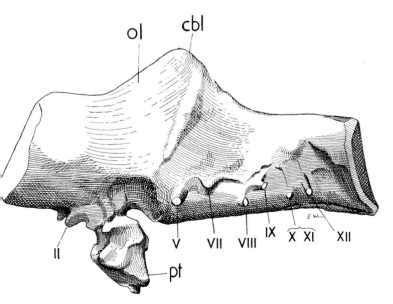

Fig. 60.—Brain cast of *Iguanodon*. cbl, cerebellum; ol, optic lobes; pt, pituitary; II–XII, cranial nerves. One-half natural size.

H

pads, ended in little hoofs. The tail was long but more laterally compressed than that of *Iguanodon*. It seems therefore that *Anatosaurus* made the best of two worlds: it was adapted for movement on the soft ground around the margins of lakes and it could escape from its flesh-eating enemies into the waters.

The arrangement of the leaf-like or lanceolate teeth in these duck-billed dinosaurs is unique. They functioned not as individuals but as a closely applied mosaic. This moved as the teeth grew, the worn teeth being discarded at the jaw's edge, and replaced by the upward growing successors. In some species the number of teeth in each half of the jaw may be up to five or six hundred, so that over two thousand teeth may have been in use simultaneously.

The Hadrosaurs are of two different kinds; hooded and unhooded. *Anatosaurus** and *Edmontosaurus** are examples of the latter. In the hooded kinds the premaxillary, nasal and frontal bones may be involved in a considerable lengthening and bending of the surface, culminating in *Parasaurolophus** where a great tube, bent upon itself, projects far behind the skull. There is no doubt that, whatever may have been the cause of this excessive growth, the nasal tube or chamber was used as an accessory supply of air when the animals submerged in the water in their search for the roots of the harsh reeds upon which they appear to have fed. That the structure was an adaptation for this purpose would seem to be borne out by the fact that all hooded Hadrosaurs have an obvious thickening at the distal end of the ischium, one of the long pendent pelvic bones, whereas the unhooded types of dinosaur never have this thickening. This may have been for additional musculature to enable the tail to propel the animal like a duck in the underwater position.

The appearance of these dinosaurs is especially well known because several specimens, that had become dried up before burial and fossilization, have been found in America. One of these is the famous "Dinosaur Mummy" from Wyoming, a cast of which is on exhibition. A specimen of *Edmontosaurus** from Alberta shows very clearly the skin pattern and ornamentation and original shape of the tail.

ARMOURED DINOSAURIA

We have seen that the carnivorous dinosaurs had their quadrupedal relations which were of great size. The bipedal Ornithopods also had their quadrupedal relatives although the relationship

PLATE 16

IGUANODON ATHERFIELDENSIS

between the latter was closer both structurally and in habits than that of the two kinds of Saurischia. None the less, the armoured dinosaurs are also notable for their bizarre appearance due to the variety of bony outgrowths on the skull or body.

Stratigraphically, the oldest of these armoured, or plated, forms is the Lower Liassic *Scelidosaurus*,* which was found in 1850 at Charmouth in Dorset. The armour is relatively feeble and its arrangement in the only specimen known in its slab of rock is not very clear. The model added to the exhibition case does, however, present the probable appearance. The armour consisted of a series of longitudinal rows of bony scutes and low spines, after the manner of crocodilian scutes, but more numerously developed. On the neck and more especially on the tail, there are series of vertical plates.

Fig. 61.—An upper tooth of *Scelidosaurus harrisoni*, Lower Lias of Charmouth; twice natural size.

The animal was about 12 feet long and comparatively low upon the ground. It was a plant-eater, like all these armoured forms (Fig. 61). The skeleton of a baby *Scelidosaurus* has been found near Charmouth in which developmental stages in the body armour can be observed.

Another British dinosaur is the peculiar *Polacanthus** (Plate 17) of the Isle of Wight. Once again, the genus is known from only one specimen and it lacks the skull and the feet. None the less, the arrangement of the bony dermal elements is clear. There was a paired series of sharply pointed spines on the back, a large plate composed of a mosaic of small bony pieces was over the lumbar region, and a paired series of spines again appeared on the tail. This arrangement, apart from the lumbar buckler, is reminiscent of a well-known American form, *Stegosaurus* (plated reptile). In this large dinosaur, sometimes nearly 30 feet long, the skull was small and probably carried low. The fore limbs were short and bent

PLATE 17

POLACANTHUS

so that the fore-quarters were comparatively near to the ground. The hind limbs, however, were large and long so that the lumbar region was quite high. Running down the centre of the back, above but in no way connected with the backbone, was a series of about twenty-two bony plates probably arranged alternately, small over the neck and gradually increasing in size and weight until they reach their maximum in a large plate about 3 feet in diameter over the pelvis. Behind this the plates again diminish, ceasing altogether about 3 feet from the end of the tail. Behind them, pointing to the end of the tail, come two pairs of long sharp spines. The great plates were only embedded in the skin, and although they might present a barrier to a large carnivore attempting to bite the backbone, they can have been little real protection, for more vulnerable parts of the body and the limbs were quite accessible to an attacker. The suggestion that the spines at the end of the tail could be used offensively if the tail were swung round sharply is contradicted by the interlocking structure of the tail vertebrae. *Stegosaurus* is best known from American specimens, but its plates have been found in England and the English *Dacentrurus* (*Omosaurus*)* is nearly related.

The ultimate in protective covering by plate, spine and ossicle is seen in *Scolosaurus** from the Upper Cretaceous of Canada.

Perhaps the most successful of the armoured types were the horned dinosaurs, or Ceratopsia, represented in the Dinosaur Gallery by some excellent skulls and other parts of the skeleton, and a cast of a complete skeleton of *Triceratops*. The geological history of the Ceratopsia begins in the Upper Cretaceous, in the Gobi Desert of Mongolia, where, in 1923, an American Museum Expedition under the leadership of Roy Chapman Andrews discovered 75 skulls and 12 skeletons of small dinosaurs with little "frilled" skulls and eggs, sometimes even containing the remains of embryos. These dinosaurs were named *Protoceratops*.* The beginnings of the neck frill are developed as bilateral extensions of the parietal bones, each being incompletely roofed so that a more or less symmetrical orifice appears on each side of a median crest. In life these openings or fontanelles were covered by skin. The nasal region of the skull of *Protoceratops*, where a horn is developed in later and larger forms, is slightly thickened. *Protoceratops* is also primitive in having teeth on the premaxillary bones as in *Hypsilophodon*. The frill at the back of the skull would seem to be developed as a base for the attachment of the head and neck muscles and not as a defensive mechanism. Exhibited specimens illustrate these points.

In the Upper Cretaceous of North America the Ceratopsia reached their maximum development. Numerous different kinds all shared the essential features of a bony frill over the neck and one or

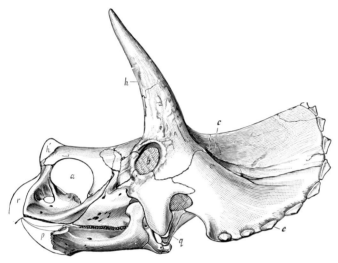

Fig. 62.—Skull and mandible of *Triceratops flabellatus*, left side view, Cretaceous of Wyoming; about one-twentieth natural size. a, nostrils; b, orbit; c, supra-temporal vacuity; e, small bony plates on margins of occipital; h, left horn core; h¹, unpaired horn core on nose; p, predentary bone; q, quadrate bone; r, rostral bone. [After Marsh.]

more horns upon the face. In *Monoclonius* there was a large nasal horn, no brow horns, and an incompletely closed frill over the neck. In *Styracosaurus* the fontanelles in the crest are closed and six long spikes project backwards from the rim of the frill. *Diceratops* has a horn above each orbit, but no nasal horn, and again fontanelles appear in the crest. In *Triceratops** (Fig. 62), perhaps the best known of them all, the openings in the frill are closed, there is a nasal horn and a horn above each eye. This dinosaur might be 30 feet long, the skull itself being 7 feet long. In general appearance the creature was not unlike a rhinoceros, and no doubt it had similar habits. It must have been a formidable opponent so long as it was able to present its head towards its adversary, and if taken from behind unawares the vulnerable region of the neck was no doubt amply protected by the great frill with its attached muscles and covering of thick skin. An interesting and unique feature of the Ceratopsian skull is the development of a rostral bone in front of the premaxillae and in opposition to the predentary below (Fig. 62).

There were Ceratopsians, such as *Torosaurus*, even larger than *Triceratops*, but the hey-day of dinosaurian expansion and growth was passing and the closing stages of the Cretaceous period in America, as elsewhere, came in a world where the reptilian dominance was greatly diminished and was soon to be lost.

XIII. FLYING REPTILES

The Mesozoic saw the reptiles not only in command of the land and the sea, but also highly successful in the air with the Order Pterosauria. Many examples of the various kinds of Pterosaurs have been found in England, Germany and in the United States, some of them in a remarkable state of preservation.

It has already been stated that the flying reptiles and the birds all originated from a Thecodont ancestor. *Euparkeria,** from the Lower Triassic of South Africa, is perhaps a distant relative though it is itself certainly not the ancestor.

The many similarities between the Pterosaurs and the birds are due more to parallel development and their adaptation to the same kind of life than to their being relics of this joint ancestry.

Since the first specimens discovered were named *Pterodactylus** by Cuvier, the name Pterodactyl has come to be used generally for all flying reptiles, although it should strictly be confined to the latest Jurassic and Cretaceous kinds.

In all flying reptiles the skeleton is very light and composed, as in flying birds, of hard and compact bone. The vertebrae and the limb bones have well-fitting joints and the limb bones are hollowed. presumably to receive air from the lungs.

The head is shaped like that of a bird and is fixed similarly at right angles to the neck. Remains have been found from which casts of the brain cavity could be made and the shape and general arrangement of the brain was similar to that of the birds. The neck was stout but mobile, the large vertebrae being joined by ball-and-socket joints, with the ball at the hinder end of each vertebra.

In Pterosaurs the body is always relatively small and the wings are disproportionately large. Sometimes the tail was long and slender and sometimes it was very short.

The wings consisted of a thin membrane supported by the greatly elongated fourth finger (Fig. 63) and without any other support in the membrane itself. The flying structure or patagium was therefore unlike that of the bird or the bat. The breast-bone is expanded in front and keeled to some extent to accommodate the muscles for flapping the wings. Generally, this power was not so well developed as in birds, and the reptiles must have floated on air currents rather than have flown by strong movements of the wings. In any case the softness of the wing skin would be much less mechanically efficient than bird or bat wings.

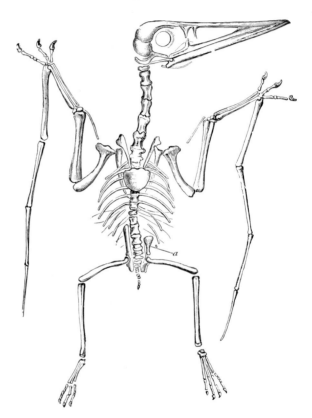

Fig. 63.—Skeleton of *Pterodactylus spectabilis*, Upper Jurassic of Bavaria; natural size. a, public bone.

The wing structure and the body outlines of many Pterodactyls are known from impressions in the fine-grained limestone, the Lithographic Stone, of Bavaria.

The earliest flying reptile known is *Dimorphodon** from the Lower Lias of Lyme Regis in Dorset. The first specimen was discovered by Mary Anning in 1828, and is exhibited in the Fossil Reptile Gallery. Its head is disproportionately large, yet remarkably light in structure, and its name is derived from the fact that the jaws had large teeth in sockets in front and small teeth behind. The hind limbs are relatively large and there is a long tail strengthened by bony tendons.

The Jurassic Pterodactyls generally are smaller than *Dimorphodon* or those that followed them in the Cretaceous. Some of the short-tailed *Pterodactylus** specimens from the Lithographic Stone are no larger than sparrows or thrushes. All have teeth in sockets and all of them have three fingers with claws adjoining the base of the wing finger. It used to be thought that the first finger or thumb

Fig. 64.—Restoration of *Rhamphorhynchus phyllurus*, Upper Jurassic of Bavaria; one-seventh natural size. [After Marsh.]

was turned back to serve as a support for the little flap of skin connecting the upper arm and the shoulder, but this is a small splint-like bone known as the pteroid and is not a true first digit. There is, however, no trace of the fifth finger.

Several skeletons from the Lithographic Stone are of a rather larger, long-tailed form, *Rhamphorhynchus.** This reptile had slender, toothed jaws that end in front in a pointed and toothless beak. It was tailed and the fine-grained rock in which some specimens have been found reveals that there was a small, diamond-shaped, rudder-like expansion to the tail. Since the tail was strengthened by strong ligaments it was presumably used as a rudder (Fig. 64).

The Pterodactyls and the Rhamphorhynchoid reptiles are all of Jurassic age; their descendants or successors in the Cretaceous were much larger, and many interesting specimens have come from the Gault and Chalk of Kent and especially from the Chalk of Kansas, U.S.A.

*Pteranodon** is the best known of these. Its jaws form a sharp toothless beak and the head rises behind in a long bony crest. The breast-bone is short and broad, with a keel in front; and the shoulder-blade on each side is firmly fixed to the backbone to make a stronger foundation on which the wing could work. The wing fingers are enormous and the wing span in some specimens was about 25 feet (Fig. 65). It is possible that some of the muscles to raise the wings were attached to the crest at the back of the head, but the crest was typical of a general lengthening of several features in the skeleton. Three little fingers, with large claws, occur as

Fig. 65.—Skeleton of *Nyctosaurus gracilis*, a crestless pteranodont, Upper Cretaceous of Kansas; about one-twentieth natural size.

splints alongside the base of the wing finger. The hind limbs, however, must have been weak and could scarcely have supported the whole weight of the animal when on the ground. In the air the flight of *Pteranodon* probably resembled that of the modern albatross. Although this form was toothless, several American contemporaries were toothed, as was *Ornithocheirus** from the English Chalk. The infilling of the thin-walled bones by chalk has preserved their shape, and sections of the bone still reveal their minute structure as well as the struts that strengthen the long bones. The Kansas Chalk specimens, although more complete, are invariably much crushed

With all these flying reptiles there are many problems in assessing their efficiency in flight. The thinness of the wing membrane, and its lack of support away from the body and the wing finger, suggest that it would be liable to many accidents both in the air and on the ground or on the surface of water. The hind limbs are nearly always apparently inadequate for movement on the ground, indeed it has been suggested that the Pterosaurs rested while hanging head downwards like bats. The smaller kinds, in the Jurassic, probably lived around lake margins, and the larger forms presumably attempted much longer flights over deeper waters.

The fact that all our Pterosaurs are from water-laid deposits leads one to speculate whether the picture is unbalanced in that the terrestrial forms have not been preserved and are thus unknown, rather than that they never existed.

XIV. THE LIZARDS AND LIZARD-LIKE REPTILES

The only major group not so far dealt with in these pages is the Lepidosauria, which had a wide range in the past, especially in Cretaceous times. With them may be grouped here the Rhynchocephalia, for they have much in common and probably shared a common ancestor.

It is not improbable that most of these animals were derived from a small reptile named *Youngina*, from the Permian of South Africa. This little reptile had a skull just over 2 inches long, furnished on each side at the back with two openings, one of them on the top of the skull, just behind the orbit, and the other placed laterally, just below it. The bar of bone separating the two openings was formed by the postorbital and squamosal bones.

EOSUCHIA

Youngina is not alone in its group, for there is another, almost certainly related, form, *Prolacerta*, from the Lower Triassic of South Africa. Until quite recently these two reptiles were regarded as belonging to the Sub-order Eosuchia of the Order Thecodontia. Now they are considered, with a number of other South African or Madagascar fossils, to make up the Order Eosuchia, which with the Rhynchocephalia and the Squamata make up a Sub-class, the Lepidosauria. They are thus clearly separated from the Pseudosuchia, with which they share some characters, the group that gave rise to the so-called ruling reptiles, the Dinosaurs, Crocodiles, Pterosaurs and the Birds. The Pseudosuchia are still classed in the Thecodontia. It is necessary to make this point, since the groups are still combined in some text-books.

From the Eosuchian stock has come a mixed assemblage of reptiles, as for example the Thalattosaurs, small marine reptiles of the American Trias, and the Champsosaurs, which were curiously crocodile-like with gavial-snouted skulls. These are known from the Cretaceous and the Eocene of North America, France and Belgium. They were small fish-eating animals at first sight rather like the Rhynchocephalians, but their teeeth were firmly placed in sockets and not fixed marginally along the jaw-bone.

RHYNCHOCEPHALIA

The Rhynchocephalia are still represented by the little burrow-dwelling reptile *Sphenodon*, the Tuatara, found on islands off the north coast of New Zealand. *Sphenodon* is a slow-moving lizard-like animal that can apparently remain quiescent for very long periods without breathing and which has on top of its head a still functional pineal "eye" or light-sensitive organ. Going back through the 180 million years or so to the Trias, one finds the Rhynchocephalia still represented by *Sphenodon*-like forms.

Such fossil genera as *Polysphenodon*, *Glevosaurus*, *Hyperodapedon*, *Rhynchosaurus* and others from the Trias of the West of England and Scotland are representative of this small kind of reptile which had a wide distribution. All of them are characterized by a beaked rostrum; some had a pineal opening, others not.

SQUAMATA

The Squamata are divided into two main groups: the Lacertilia or Lizards, and the Serpentes or Snakes. The former seem to be derived from a form like the Eosuchian *Prolacerta*, and the earliest known true lizards are the Triassic specialized gliders *Kuehneosaurus* from England and *Icarosaurus* from New Jersey. Even so, it is not until much later that remains become at all common. The Jurassic *Ardeosaurus* may be an ancestor of the skinks, though these are not known much before the Eocene. Iguanas and slow-worms were, however, fairly widely distributed by the Cretaceous. *Iguana* itself, now characteristic of the tropical regions of America, was common in the Upper Eocene of Hampshire. Later varanids or monitors attained considerable size and *Megalania prisca*, of the Pleistocene of Australia, was several times as large as the normal living varanid and approached some of the Komodo dragons in length.

In the Cretaceous there were two kinds of swimming lizards; the first group comprising small reptiles which are named Dolichosauria in allusion to their elongated shape They had a vertebral column much like that of a snake, and it is doubtful if they were more than semi-aquatic *Dolichosaurus* itself is found in the Chalk of Kent and is nearly 3 feet long, and *Adriosaurus*, from the Lower Cretaceous of Hvar Island in Yugoslavia, is about 18 inches long.

117

Contrasting greatly with these in size and in distribution are the Mosasaurs, the great lizards of the sea which in a relatively short period of geological time attained a world-wide distribution. Their skull resembles that of the living lizard quite closely, but the palate bears recurved teeth and the jaws are as loose as those of snakes for swallowing bulky prey. The large and conical teeth are very characteristically fixed by their swollen bases to the supporting jaws. The eyes, like those of so many reptiles ashore and afloat, had sclerotic plates.

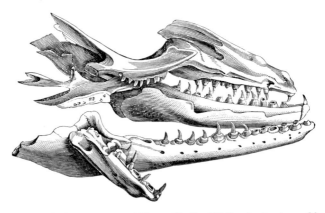

Fig. 66.—Jaws of *Mosasaurus camperi*, Upper Chalk of Holland; about one-fifteenth natural size.

The vertebrae are also highly characteristic and are unlike those of other fossil reptiles, for though they articulate by a ball-and-socket joint, the ball is shallow and is unmistakable in appearance. The limbs, though essentially lacertilian, are modified into paddles, the paddle bones bieng the fingers and toes lengthened and the joints increased in number. These show a third method of adaptation of the limbs for life in the sea, and do not closely resemble the limbs of the Ichthyosaurs and Plesiosaurs. So far as is known there was no armour in the skin, though there may have been thin scales.

The typical genus is *Mosasaurus* itself (Fig. 66); the name being derived from the river Meuse, in whose valley near Maastricht the Chalk first yielded its remains.

Since that date many specimens have been found in Europe, Africa, America and even New Zealand. *Mosasaurus** and allied genera like *Leiodon* and *Tylosaurus* were all large animals reaching about 50 feet long. Others, such as *Platecarpus* (Fig. 67) and *Clidastes* were smaller, and the latter appears to have developed a tail fin to assist movement in the water.

The Snakes or Ophidia are the last members of this group with which we need deal and they are not very well represented in the geological record. In the South of England *Palaeophis*, a sea-snake, was fairly common and many remains, mostly vertebrae (Fig. 68), have been found in the Eocene London Clay of the Isle of Sheppey. Fragments of another, larger sea-snake known as *Pterosphenus* come from the Eocene of Alabama, U.S.A., and of the Fayum in Egypt. The largest snake was a kind of python, *Gigantophis garstoni*, known from vertebrae and a small piece of jaw found in the Middle Eocene of the Fayum. This snake may have been 60 feet long. The grass snakes and their relatives seem to have come into the record in the Oligocene, and the poison-bearing snakes, with their grooved or hollow fangs, are of Miocene date. Unfortunately, though the fossil record of the Ophidia dates from the Cretaceous, it is very incomplete and many interesting problems of their evolution and geographical distribution cannot yet be solved.

J

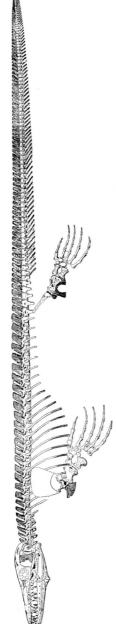

Fig. 67.—Skeleton of *Platecarpus coryphaeus*, Upper Cretaceous of Kansas; about one-twenty-fifth natural size. [After Williston.]

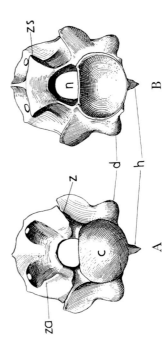

Fig. 68.—Anterior trunk vertebra of *Palaeophis*. A, anterior view; B, posterior view; c, centrum; d, diapophysis; h, hypapophysis; n, neural canal; z, zygapophysis; za, zygantrum; zs, zygosphene. One and a half times natural size.

XV. EXTINCTION

The problem of extinction does not concern only the amphibians and reptiles. Throughout the long course of geological history many groups have died and disappeared without leaving direct descendants. Death is inevitable for all animals, but most of them leave progeny to carry on their race. In the past, however, there have been many groups composed of a large number of genera and species apparently well adapted to their habitats and with a long history of successful life which have become extinct, that is to say, have died out, leaving no representative or modified descendant.

In the case of reptiles, which have had a history on land, in the sea and in the air lasting over 200 million years, we find that many of the major groups disappeared towards the close of the Cretaceous epoch. This mass disappearance of dominant animals is a striking phenomenon and several hypotheses have been put forward to explain it.

The life of an animal or of a group of similar animals is a complex of both internal and external factors. It is obvious that animals affected by some hereditary disease may die out. It is equally obvious that animals which are unable to meet the competition of their contemporaries or, for one reason or another, are unable to adapt themselves to changing circumstances may be compelled to give up the struggle and die. Life might be defined as the struggle between an organism and its environment, and this environment consists not only of the other plants and animals with which the animal is brought into association, and which may be enemies or food or even forms of disease, but also includes the climate; that is, heat and cold, drought, moisture and the amount of sunlight. Geographical factors, such as altered distribution of land and water and other changes, also affect the problem.

Within the animal itself there may be either progressive or retrogressive trends. An animal of retrogressive trends without a good deal of physiological plasticity would find it difficult to adapt itself to rapidly changing climatic and geographical circumstances and therefore might die out.

An examination of the wide field of vertebrate palaeontology shows that all of these factors have operated from time to time, but there is no evidence that cataclysm has ever been the cause of extinction at any time anywhere. Flood or earthquake, volcanic action or epidemic disease may have destroyed comparatively small communities, but have not led to the extinction of any major group.

Excessive competition is sometimes emphasized, especially with new and higher types. This competition between animals and the fight for food are features that have affected all forms of life throughout the ages, but need not necessarily result in extinction. The possibility has been mooted that many reptilian groups became extinct because of the depredations of egg-eating mammals; this suggestion may be classed with the cataclysmic forces as being responsible for occasional diminution in numbers on a small scale, but not for any general disappearance. Of much greater significance are those causes which are in the make-up of the animal; that is to say, the anatomical or physiological factors that may have predisposed certain groups to extinction. For example, it has been suggested that endocrine disease, disorder of the highly important ductless glands, has been responsible for the disappearance of groups of dinosaurs. The effects of over-activity of certain endocrine glands, or on the other hand of endocrine deficiencies, might have influenced the viability of some of the older groups in changing environmental circumstances. The increase of size which follows pituitary over-activity would involve among other things the need for greater food supplies. There might also be a decrease in the number of young produced and an increase in the length of time taken by the young to reach maturity. This would be a serious defect, since the combined death rate and infantile mortality rate would wipe out any reserve of population, but it is likely to be much more serious in mammals than in the reptiles and its results would be gradual rather than sudden in their operation. Another aspect of such hyper-activity would be extensive deposition of bone in the skeleton or in accessory structures, such as is obvious in some of the Upper Cretaceous dinosaurs. Some of this secondary matter must have been a considerable hindrance to its possessors, but it is doubtful if it formed in itself a cause of extinction.

Before the beginning of the Tertiary period many major groups of reptiles became extinct, though a few orders living apparently under similar circumstances were able to survive and to give rise to the reptiles of today. During Upper Cretaceous (Cenomanian) times there were profound geological changes involving widespread invasion of the land by the sea, collectively known as the Cenomanian transgression. Lagoons, estuaries and pools that had long been the living-places of many reptiles were overwhelmed by deep waters: swamps and low-lying areas were rendered uninhabitable.

Alterations of habits or of habitat may not be serious difficulties to young and vigorous stocks, but the reptiles at the end of the Cretaceous belonged for the most part to lineages that had lost their plasticity, showing signs of an old-age degeneracy such as lack of teeth and development of supplementary bone and horn. In changing conditions, gigantic size and over-specialization are great drawbacks. Apart then from any direct extermination of sections of the population, there would be fiercer competition between various groups of reptiles themselves, and between reptiles and birds. Competition with the mammals is sometimes cited as a contributory factor, but is is doubtful if this was ever more than it is at present. At the time when the major reptilian groups were disappearing, the mammals had been in existence for at least 100 million years. As the reptiles disappeared they were replaced by mammals; it was more a repopulation than a mammalian victory. Similarly in the plant kingdom, when the earth movements which caused the Cenomanian transgression were eventually reversed, the re-emerging land was rapidly colonized by the flowering plants, and the old Mesozoic vegetation, already losing ground, almost disappeared. Thus, for herbivorous reptiles there was a change or diminution in the food supply to which they had long been accustomed. Furthermore, in certain parts of their world, as in the north of America, the new vegetation was without green leaves or shoots for several months of the year, a change which was correlated with altering climate. If the herbivores diminished, or died out, the carnivores that preyed on them would be affected.

Thus the factors that led to extinction are many and complex. No one theory, no single event, can explain the disappearance during the closing stages of the Cretaceous and the dawn of the Eocene of groups that had hitherto had a long record of dominance. It may be perhaps, that dominance itself is impermanent, for the organisms that have survived for the longest periods of geological time have usually been, like the little brachiopod *Lingula*, obscure and unobtrusive.

GEOLOGICAL TIME-SCALE†

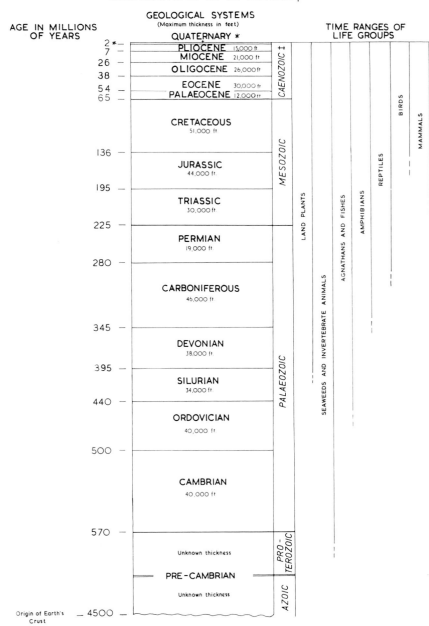

| AGE IN MILLIONS OF YEARS | GEOLOGICAL SYSTEMS (Maximum thickness in feet) | | TIME RANGES OF LIFE GROUPS |

GEOLOGICAL SYSTEMS
(Maximum thickness in feet)

AGE IN MILLIONS OF YEARS

TIME RANGES OF LIFE GROUPS

QUATERNARY *

| 2 *— |
7 —	PLIOCENE 15,000 ft
26 —	MIOCENE 21,000 ft
38 —	OLIGOCENE 26,000 ft
54 —	EOCENE 30,000 ft
65 —	PALAEOCENE 12,000 ft

CAENOZOIC ‡

CRETACEOUS 51,000 ft

136 —

JURASSIC 44,000 ft

195 —

TRIASSIC 30,000 ft

MESOZOIC

225 —

PERMIAN 19,000 ft

280 —

CARBONIFEROUS 46,000 ft

345 —

DEVONIAN 38,000 ft

395 —

SILURIAN 34,000 ft

PALAEOZOIC

440 —

ORDOVICIAN 40,000 ft

500 —

CAMBRIAN 40,000 ft

570 —

Unknown thickness

PRE-CAMBRIAN

Unknown thickness

PRO-TEROZOIC

AZOIC

Origin of Earth's Crust — 4500 —

Life groups: SEAWEEDS AND INVERTEBRATE ANIMALS · AGNATHANS AND FISHES · LAND PLANTS · AMPHIBIANS · REPTILES · BIRDS · MAMMALS

† Time-scale approximate with probable error of ± 5% throughout
✗ Quaternary (Pleistocene and Holocene) 6,000 feet +
‡ Caenozoic = Tertiary (Palaeocene - Pliocene) + Quaternary
Column proportional to time-scale

CLASSIFICATION OF FOSSIL AMPHIBIANS AND REPTILES

CLASS AMPHIBIA
  SUPER-ORDER Labyrinthodontia

	ORDER Ichthyostegalia	Devonian–Carboniferous
	ORDER Rhachitomi	Carboniferous–Lower Trias
	ORDER Stereospondyli	Triassic
Sub-class Apsidospondyli	ORDER Embolomeri	Carboniferous–Lower Permian
	ORDER Seymouriamorpha	Permian
	SUPER-ORDER Salientia	
	ORDER Eoanura	Carboniferous
	ORDER Proanura	Lower Trias
	ORDER Anura	Upper Jurassic to Recent

	ORDER Aistopoda	Carboniferous
	ORDER Nectridia	Upper Carboniferous–Lower Permian
Sub-class Lepospondyli	ORDER Microsauria	Carboniferous to Upper Permian
	ORDER Urodela	Lower Cretaceous–Recent
	ORDER Apoda	Recent

CLASS REPTILIA

Sub-class Anapsida	ORDER Cotylosauria	
	Sub-order Captorhinomorpha	Carboniferous–Lower Permian
	Sub-order Diadectomorpha	Carboniferous–Upper Triassic
	ORDER Chelonia	
	Sub-order Eunotosauria	Middle Permian
	Sub-order Amphichelydia	Upper Triassic–Pleistocene
	Sub-order Pleurodira	Upper Cretaceous–Recent
	Sub-order Cryptodira	Upper Jurassic to Recent
Sub-class Ichthyopterygia	ORDER Ichthyosauria	Triassic–Upper Cretaceous
Sub-class Synaptosauria	ORDER Protorosauria	Lower Permian–Upper Triassic
	ORDER Sauropterygia	
	Sub-order Nothosauria	Triassic
	Sub-order Plesiosauria	Middle Triassic–Upper Cretaceous
	Sub-order Placodontia	Triassic
Sub-class Lepidosauria	ORDER Eosuchia	Upper Permian–Eocene
	ORDER Rhynchocephalia	Lower Triassic–Recent
	ORDER Squamata	
	Sub-order Lacertilia	Upper Triassic–Recent
	Infra-order Platynota	Cretaceous–Recent
	Sub-order Serpentes	Lower Cretaceous–Recent
Sub-class Archosauria	ORDER Thecodontia	
	Sub-order Pseudosuchia	Triassic
	Sub-order Phytosauria	Triassic
	ORDER Crocodilia	
	Sub-order Protosuchia	Upper Tarissic
	Sub-order Mesosuchia	Lower Jurassic–Eocene
	Sub-order Eusuchia	Upper Jurassic–Recent
	ORDER Pterosauria	
	Sub-order Rhamphorynchoidea	Jurassic
	Sub-order Pterodactyloidea	Upper Jurassic–Upper Cretaceous
	ORDER Saurischia	
	Sub-order Theropoda	Triassic–Cretaceous
	Sub-order Sauropoda	Lower Jurassic–Upper Cretaceous
	ORDER Ornithischia	
	Sub-order Ornithopoda	Upper Triassic–Upper Cretaceous
	Sub-order Stegosauria	Lower Jurassic–Lower Cretaceous
	Sub-order Ankylosauria	Lower Cretaceous–Upper Cretaceous
	Sub-order Ceratopsia	Upper Cretaceous
Sub-class Synapsida	ORDER Pelycosauria	
	Sub-order Ophiacodontia	Upper Carboniferous–Middle Permian
	Sub-order Sphenacodontia	Upper Carboniferous–Lower Triassic
	Sub-order Edaphosauria	Upper Carboniferous–Upper Permian
	ORDER Therapsida	
	Sub-order Dinocephalia	Middle Permian
	Sub-order Dicynodontia	Middle Permian–Upper Triassic
	Sub-order Theriodontia	Middle Permian–Middle Triassic
	ORDER Ictidosauria	Lower Triassic–Middle Jurassic

GLOSSARY

Acetabulum. The cup-shaped hollow or the notch in the pelvis for the head of the femur or thigh-bone. In fossil reptiles it is usually part of the ilium.

Allantois. A great development of the urinary bladder that grows outside the body of the embryo to lie under the outer layer of the yolk sac just inside the shell. It is richly supplied with blood-vessels and respiration takes place through these vessels in the developing reptile.

Amnion. The sac that encloses the unborn young is lined with the *amnion*, though the name is often given to the whole sac. The fluid (amniotic fluid) in the sac allows the young reptile or bird to develop in the egg although on dry land.

Articular. One of the bones of the lower jaw and that which, in reptiles, always articulates with the quadrate above.

Articulation. The surface for the movement of one bone on another, or the movement itself.

Carina. A keel; a term applied in fossil reptiles to the slight ridge or edge on one or two (inner or outer; front or back) sides of teeth. Sometimes used for the keel for attachment of muscles on the breast-bone.

Carpal. One of the bones of the wrist.

Caudal. Of the tail; e.g. caudal vertebra.

Cenomanian. Period of the Upper Cretaceous during which extensive encroachment of waters on the land took place.

Centrum. The body or cylindrical portion of a vertebra.

Cerebellum. Part of the brain concerned with special muscular co-ordination. In reptiles it is a comparatively small outgrowth of the upper surface of the hinder part of the brain. (Cf. Cerebrum.)

Cerebrum. The paired front parts or lobes of the upper surface of the brain. They are used in co-ordination.

Cervical. Of the neck; e.g. cervical vertebrae.

Clavicle. One of the bones of the shoulder girdle, on the front or ventral side. In man it is the collar-bone. In the reptiles it has been lost in the dinosaurs, crocodiles and chameleons.

Cleidoic. "Enclosed" egg like that of birds and reptiles in which the fluid for the embryo is contained in a more or less impermeable shell.

Cleithrum. A large upper bone in the shoulder girdle of fishes and primitive amphibians. It lies above the clavicle and in the most primitive amphibia has still some connexion with the skull. The bone is found in primitive Chelonia and in Pelycosaurs.

Cold-bloodied. Characteristic of living fishes, amphibia and reptiles, in which the body temperature is not constant but varies to some extent with that of the surroundings. Reptiles acquire heat directly from their surroundings or by exertion, and lose it by radiation or conduction.

Condyle. A projection or knob of bone which moves in a depression or cup in another bone; e.g. condyle of skull which allows skull to move on the neck.

Convergence. The gradual approach in similarity or general appearance of two or more groups, due to the adoption of the same habits and environment and not due to relationship; e.g. fishes and ichthyosaurs; ichthyosaurs and dolphins; pterodactyls and birds.

Coracoid. One of the lower (ventral) bones of the shoulder girdle, which helps with the scapula in the formation of the glenoid cavity (q.v.).

Costal. Of the ribs. The plates overlying the ribs in the upper shell (carapace) of a Chelonian.

Dentary. The tooth-bearing bone of the lower jaw.

Digit. A finger or toe. Each digit contains one or more phalanges.

Diphyodont. Having only two sets of teeth in the jaws; e.g. milk (or child) series and adult series. Mammals and some of the mammal-like reptiles are diphyodont. (Cf. Polyphyodont.).

Dipnoans. Lung fishes; well known in the fossil record and still represented by living forms in South Africa, South America and Australia.

Distal. Away from the body or point of attachment; e.g. distal end of the leg is at the foot. (Cf. Proximal.)

Dorsal. Upper surface (back) of a crawling animal's body or backward surface of a biped. Dorsal vertebrae are those of the trunk, between the cervicals and lumbars.

Entoplastron. A median, unpaired and usually small plate near the front end of the lower shell (plastron) of Chelonians. It is thought to represent the interclavicle of most other reptiles.

Epiplastron. The foremost of the paired series of plates on the chelonian ventral shield or plastron, thought to be the remnant of the clavicles.

Femur. The thigh-bone.

Fibula. The outer and hinder bone of the two in the lower leg. See Tibia.

Fontanelle. An opening in the skull that was covered only by skin during life. The openings in the neck-frill of horned dinosaurs are often known as fontanelles.

Foramen magnum. The opening at the back or base of the skull through which the spinal, or nerve, cord issues.

Gait. Method or style of walking.

Gape. Amount to which the jaws can open.

Genus. A unit in classification. A genus consists of one or more species. One or more genera make a family. With the name of the Nile Crocodile *Crocodylus niloticus*, the *whole* name is the specific name, but *Crocodylus* itself is the name of the genus. In the scientific literature the name of genus and species is printed, usually, in italics.

Girdle. The bones constituting the shoulder and pelvic regions to ensure support of the body and attachment of the limbs are known as girdles; viz. shoulder girdle and pelvic girdle.

Glenoid cavity. The cavity or space into which the head of the humerus (or upper arm-bone) fits and turns. It is composed in the amphibia and reptilia generally of part of the scapula or adjacent parts of the scapula and coracoid.

Heterodont. Teeth of different kinds: incisors, canines, premolars and molars.

Humerus. The upper arm-bone. Connects with the glenoid fossa at its head and with radius and ulna distally.

Hyoid arch. Composed of hyomandibular (q.v.), which is the upper part, and the hyoid bone which remains as a support of the tongue in tetrapods.

Hyomandibular. Upper part of the fish hyoid arch: part of the jaw suspension in fish but transformed into stapes of ear in amphibia and reptiles.

Hypoplastron. One of the median of the four or five paired plates of the chelonian undershield or plastron: they are epiplastron, hyoplastron, mesoplastron, hypoplastron and xiphiplastron (Fig. 25).

Hypoplastron. One of the plates of the chelonian plastron. See under Hyoplastron.

Ilium. The uppermost of the three bones forming each side of the pelvic girdle. It is joined to one or more of the sacral vertebrae and usually provides part of the cup or acetabulum for the head of the femur.

Incipient. Structure showing promise of development or greater use or importance. Primitive condition of structure whose fuller development is known in later forms.

Intercentrum. One of the two elements in the development of the vertebral body. It plays a role of varied importance in the amphibia (Fig. 5).

Interclavicle. Part of the shoulder girdle, in front between the clavicles or collarbones. In some fossil amphibia it is very large.

Ischium. The hinder and lower of the three bones forming each side of the pelvic girdle. It usually helps to form the acetabulum for the head of the femur.

Labyrinthodontia. A large group of fossil amphibia characterized by having teeth with an involved or labyrinthine folding of the dentine.

Lumbar. The region between the dorsal or thoracic vertebrae and the sacral. In reptiles the lumbar vertebrae often have ribs, but in mammals they bear none.

Marginal. One of the plates lining the edge of the chelonian carapace.

Mesoplastron. One of the median plates of the chelonian plastron. See under Hyoplastron.

Nares. The openings in the skull for the external nostrils.

Neopallium. Part of the roof of the brain; formed on the cerebral hemispheres. Receives impressions from centres other than the olfactory.

Neural. Neural process: the part of the vertebral structure around and above the spinal cord. Neural plate: one of the line of (usually) eight plates on the carapace immediately above the dorsal vertebrae of the Chelonia (Figs. 5, 24).

Notochord. The central rod or cord which in adult animals is invested almost completely by vertebrae.

Nuchal. The anterior, median, plate of the chelonian carapace; it precedes the neurals.

Occipital condyle. See Condyle.

Olecranon. The elbow joint process of the ulna: the "funny bone".

Operculum. The gill cover in the fishes and amphibians.

Otic notch. Notch in the hind border of the Stegocephalian skull. Bounded by tabular, supratemporal and squamosal bones. It may be open or it may become closed through growth of bone on its outer side. Sometimes called auditory notch.

Ovo-viviparous. Condition in which the eggs hatch out in the body of the mother, and the young are born alive: found in lizards, snakes and ichthyosaurs.

Patagium. The wing membrane of the flying and gliding reptiles.

Pectoral girdle. The shoulder girdle, providing attachment to the fore-limb bones and muscles and the breast-bone and muscles.

Pelvic girdle. The hip-bones, giving attachment so the hind leg bones and muscles.

Phalange. A bone or "joint" in a finger or toe.

Pineal foramen. The opening seen in fossil amphibians and many reptilian skulls for the eye formed by the pineal gland on the upper surface of the brain.

Plastron. The lower shell of the chelonian.

Pleurocentrum. One of the structures forming (with the intercentrum) the vertebrae of Labyrinthodont amphibia.

Polyphyodont. Condition in which teeth are constantly replaced, as in nearly all reptiles, and not limited to one or two dentitions.

Predentary. Anterior bone of the lower jaw in Ornithischian dinosaurs. It is toothless.

Proximal. Nearest to the place of attachment to the body; e.g. proximal part of arm is at shoulder. (Cf. Distal.)

Pubis. Forward and lower bone on each side of pelvis, usually directed forward, downwards and inwards to meet its fellow of the other side.

Pygal. Hindermost median plate of chelonian carapace: behind neurals (Fig. 24).

Quadrate. Bone at the hinder end, on each side, of the upper jaw. In all reptiles articulates with the articular bone of lower jaw.

Quadrato-jugal. Bone in front of quadrate on side of skull. Not present in most plesiosaurs.

Radius. The inner of the two lower arm-bones.

Rostral. Anterior median bone in upper jaw of Ceratopsian dinosaurs. It is toothless.

Sacrum. Formed by the union of a number of vertebrae whose lateral processes are attached to the ilium. It thus binds together the dorsal parts of the pelvic girdle.

Species. The least of the commonly used terms of classification; written as two latinized words as *Crocodylus niloticus*, the Nile Crocodile. Members of a species can breed together to produce fertile offspring.

Spiracle. The remnant of the hyoid gill-slit of many fishes. In amphibia and reptiles is represented by the otic notch and the middle ear space.

Stapes. Bony rod connecting ear-drum and the inner ear, transmitting sound vibrations. It is the modified hyomandibular of the fish.

Supratemporal fossa. An opening on the upper surface of the skull of many reptiles: bounded usually by postorbital, postfrontal, parietal and squamosal bones. It is used for the attachment of muscles for the lower jaw.

Tarsal. Of the tarsus or ankle joint.

Taxonomy. The science of classification of animals and plants.

Temporal fossa. Opening on the upper surface or the side of the skull behind the orbit. The arrangement of such fossae is used in reptilian classification (Fig. 14).

Tetrapod. Literally, a four-footed animal. Used scientifically to include amphibia, reptiles, birds and mammals.

Tibia. The shin-bone; the principal bone of the lower leg.

Tympanum. The ear-drum.

Ulna. The outer or hinder of the lower arm-bones.

Vector. Animal or plant carrying germs or other matter causing disease.

Ventral. The lower surface of an animal; or of its bones; i.e. the surface nearer the ground in a quadruped and the front surface of a biped. Opposite to dorsal.

Vestigial. Remnant of a structure once of use but now disused or unimportant; e.g. pineal eye in many reptiles, vermiform appendix in man.

Viviparous. The young being developed in close association with the mother, and not in an egg or within an egg membrane up to the time of birth. The condition in most mammals.

Warm-blooded. The condition, as in birds and mammals, where the temperature of the body is usually constant and is not dependent on the environmental conditions.

Xiphiplastron. One of the hinder plates of a chelonian plastron (Fig. 25).

INDEX

Index

Index